W9-BFE-375

SCIENCE AND RELIGION

IS VOLUME

130

OF THE

Twentieth Century Encyclopedia of Catholicism

UNDER SECTION

XIII

CATHOLICISM AND SCIENCE

IT IS ALSO THE

89TH

VOLUME IN ORDER OF PUBLICATION

Edited by **HENRI DANIEL-ROPS** *of the Académie Française*

SCIENCE AND RELIGION

By DR. PAUL CHAUCHARD

Translated from the French by S. J. TESTER

HAWTHORN BOOKS · PUBLISHERS · *New York*

Copyright © 1962 by Hawthorn Books, Inc., 70 Fifth Avenue, New York 11, N.Y. Copyright under International and Pan-American Copyright Conventions. Philippines Copyright 1962 by Hawthorn Books, Inc. All rights reserved, including the right to reproduce this book, or portions thereof, in any form, except for the inclusion of brief quotations in a review. This book was manufactured in the United States of America and published simultaneously in Canada by McClelland & Stewart, Ltd., 25 Hollinger Road, Toronto 16. It was originally published in France under the title *La Science détruit-elle la Religion?*, © Librairie Arthème Fayard, 1958. The Library of Congress has catalogued The Twentieth Century Encyclopedia of Catholicism under card number 58-14327. Library of Congress Catalogue card number for this volume: 62-16132. The Catholic University of America Library has catalogued this volume based on the Lynn-Peterson Alternative Classification for Catholic Books: BQT184.T9v.130/BQT237.C49. Suggested decimal classification for this book: 215.

First Edition, July, 1962

NIHIL OBSTAT

Carolus Davis, S.T.L.

Censor Deputatus

IMPRIMATUR

E. Morrogh Bernard

Vicarius Generalis

Westmonasterii, die XIV APRILIS, MCMLXII

The Nihil obstat and Imprimatur are a declaration that a book or pamphlet is considered to be free from doctrinal or moral error. It is not implied that those who have granted the Nihil obstat and Imprimatur agree with the contents, opinions, or statements expressed.

CONTENTS

INTRODUCTION

At the beginning of this century, when science was advancing in triumph and Zola was prophesying the imminent happiness of mankind saved by science, it necessarily implied the retreat and finally the complete disappearance of religion, and especially of Catholicism. "Science suddenly irrupted into our ideas, with mass and energy, irresistible energy with a sovereign, irresistible force. And not only Catholicism was swept away like the dust of fallen buildings, but all religion, all ideas of a divinity tottered and fell." In the blessed City of his third gospel, Labour, a garden of delight was planted on the ruins of the last church, collapsed on the last priest, on "the debris of a religion of misery and death". In the face of such utter rationalism, such complete positivism, religious thinkers reacted in defence either by speaking of the "bankruptcy of science" or, like Bergson, by playing down the rôle of reason. On the one hand, the Modernists tried to adapt religion, and even to modify its doctrines, while many intellectual Christians found their own private solution by strictly separating "the oratory from the laboratory", the first often becoming merely a refuge for feelings and emotions, from which reason was rigidly excluded. On the other hand the Church, while rightly and firmly defending the unchangeable essence of religion, preserving that necessary balance between reason and faith which maintains and unites the apparently conflicting truths of rationalism and fideism, could no longer make herself understood, despite a remarkable revival of Thomist thought. Her struggle against the Modernists appeared to many people anti-scientific, in spite of her efforts to distinguish Modernism from science. In theory the distinction was simple and clear, but in the confusion of the struggle it was often obscured by a fog of tragic misunderstanding.

How far away that time now seems! Yet the various movements of sixty years ago are still active today. For more than ten years, on countless occasions, Pope Pius XII never failed, when receiving specialists in the various sciences, to emphasize the importance of the most recent developments in each, showing how each fitted in with the Christian religion, and how that religion could help each to direct itself more effectively to the service of mankind. The independence of science and the fact that the value of any scientific discovery does not depend on the personal philosophy of the discoverer were both clearly recognized, as for example when the pope remarked on the value of Pavlov's method for painless childbirth. Pius XII spoke of science with a special understanding well suited to our times, but in terms none of his predecessors would have disowned: "The scientist, as he strives to investigate the boundless resources of animate and inanimate nature, daily discovers more and more of the treasures hidden in the world by the Creator. He is, as it were, the discoverer of new lands for the greater glory of his Lord; and he is also, to the same extent, the benefactor of his fellow-men, at whose service he puts the results of his work."

The Catholic scientist no longer feels in any way less of a scientist than his agnostic colleagues. The fact that he is a Catholic does not inhibit his research or his scientific initiative. Nor does his science in any way separate him from his fellow Catholics. He is no longer cut off on his own, trying to ignore an irrational division in his own heart and mind: he is one of a community of men for whom science and religion not only do not oppose but actually complete one another. For some ten years there has flourished in England an active Philosophy of Science Group of the Newman Association. Its members try to live in the union of their science and their religion. This union raises problems, but these problems create no false dichotomy because the aim is to understand how different views of the same reality fit together. There is no confusion of ways of knowing: and if the attempt is made to distinguish them more precisely, they are nevertheless not separated. Knowing by faith all that man really is enables the specialist in human biology to advance his research into man in his biological aspect; knowing all physical reality through his science improves his understanding, within the faith, of God and his creative act.

In 1900 science seemed to carry in itself the promise of happiness for mankind. Today, in our atomic age, when a psycho-biological determinism seems to take away man's humanity, pessimism is more natural. Yet nothing would be more wrong than to base the renewal of religion on fear of science, or on assertions that science has had to withdraw before the "unknowable", that the growth of its technological power has been parallelled by the decline of its value as explanation. Whatever those think who would base religion on the irrational or on the so-called "gaps" in determinism—which are only the temporary difficulties of a difficult field—it is, on the contrary, precisely because of the enormous increase in the value of science as explaining the world and man that we can remove many of the difficulties concerning religion. The contemporary Catholic scientist can be as enthusiastically optimistic as any of former times, but he can also be more realistic. He is aware of the difficulties, and knows that the right use of science requires him to choose, to enlist freely in the service of man: it is precisely this which his religion both demands and facilitates.

Science is confined to the study of the various aspects of the physical universe. This universe it not only breaks down by a process of analysis, but must also try to reconstruct by a process of general synthesis, which is proper to it and distinct from the task of philosophy. It can never encounter spirit as such, the human soul or God. Nevertheless, the more science comprehends the complexity of the world, and the closer it approaches to God, the more is his presence felt immanent in his creation. As Pius XII said, the more progress true science makes, the more it discovers God, as if he were waiting and watching behind each door science opens. We must, of course, be on our guard against so-called scientific proofs of the existence of God. That is a problem for the philosopher. Nothing could be more risky than to base one's belief in God on a scientific hypothesis or theory which tomorrow will be changed or refuted. Yet, as Teilhard de Chardin said: "He who is is not only here, or here: the summits whereon he dwells are not inaccessible peaks but the deepest centres of things. The secret of the world is anywhere where we come to see the universe as transparent."

So science will go forward and draw nearer to God. For the vision of God, however, a certain movement of the will, of love, will always be necessary. This is the spirit of philosophy, and also grace, and must always be wanting in the rationalist mind which idolatrously worships reason instead of simply using it. The Christian scientist, therefore, who at the end of his work finds and adores the God he knows by faith, must sadly recognize—for this is the cross he must bear —that what is evident to his own reason seems out of the reach of his agnostic colleague, even though they share the same scientific outlook. His task is to render that evidence available to the other, without diminishing either the action of grace or the other's freedom.

At this very time when science and religion seem to have come together again, scientific atheism appears to be making more progress than ever. In its Marxist form it wields political power over a great part of the earth. While it puts forward a very realistic view of the world, one often based on a truly scientific outlook, it teaches that religion is merely the outmoded survival of the way of thinking of pre-scientific ages. There is no need to persecute it: it is quite enough to propagate the scientific description and explanation of the world and of man, to encourage the teaching of science and especially of the biological sciences, and religion will disappear for ever. Now we must certainly not underestimate the dangers inherent in Marxist anti-religious arguments based on science. They may be ineffectual among those who can distinguish scientific facts and theories from their anti-religious interpretation, but they are very dangerous among those who cannot make this distinction. The danger is increased if religious counter-apologetics rashly carries the argument on to the scientific level and refuses to recognize that it has stepped beyond the limits of its proper competence.

To the question, "Does science destroy religion?" rationalists and Marxists both answer, yes. They may often do this in perfectly good faith, yet they must nevertheless, if not actually distort science, at least give it a particular slant, and, without realizing it, pass from the truly scientific level to that of anti-religious philosophical interpretation. Above all, they are bound to attack not true religion, but a false one mistaken for the true—the picture they have of that false religion being very often provided for them by Christians. The more Christians lack scientific and religious education, the more susceptible they are to atheist propaganda.

To the same question, the Christian must reply, no. But to be quite certain in his denial, to avoid the suspicion that scientists—even Christian scientists—compromise to some extent with materialism, he has to learn to recognize and distinguish the different viewpoints of science and religion. He can then see that those facts and theories which are apparently most materialistic may be precisely those most charged, in all the clarity of their scientific explanation, with a profound and metaphysical power of revealing God. The arguments of atheist propaganda will then be for him only more reasons for believing; being but the denunciation of that which is not his God, the true God whom he must ever know better if he would keep his faith, they will serve to make him believe more firmly and more profoundly. So to anti-religious scientific apologetics there should be opposed an objectively scientific apologetics which can reassess it all and state clearly what belongs to science and what to religion. Such an apologetics, while seeming to be indifferent, will, in fact, end by bringing us nearer to God than any of the fine but useless arguments of an apologetics which misrepresents science or relies on its temporary and passing insufficiencies.

Today, science is concerned with so many important human problems that we can no longer think of separating the two distinct ways of knowing, science and religion. We can no longer keep our religion by remaining in ignorance of science. Every believing Christian ought to be enough of a scientist and enough of a theologian to avoid having to yield to grossly over-simplified arguments. And all scientists and theologians ought, while respecting both the independence of science and the authority of the Church in matters of religion, to collaborate in the philosophical task of producing an apologetics based on science—which is not, let us be quite clear, the whole of apologetics.[1]

Our task is to define the relations between science and religion so as to see how to avoid the destruction of religion by science. In doing this, we could set out point by point the various aspects of the scientific and religious world-pictures and discuss at a fundamental level the areas of disagreement. But it may perhaps be both more interesting and more profitable to set out in order the various positions taken up by those who reflect on the relations between science and religion. These positions not only have a historical significance but are tacitly assumed by many thinking people today. They are daily temptations for us, which we must fully understand if we are to establish ourselves in the only position which is both satisfying to us and at the same time best in accordance with the mind of the Church.

We shall look first at the denial of religion made by scientific rationalism of the old kind, based on a mechanistic materialism no longer really scientific. Then we shall examine the Marxist denial, based on a dialectical materialism which is scientifically realistic, but which because of its philosophical insufficiencies has not been able to reconcile the autonomy and the interdependence of man. In the second part we shall examine the agnostic and fideist positions of those who think that each, science and religion, has its own separate and private domain, and that a man can profess both without worrying about the relations between them. There is a sort of rationalist agnosticism which is really atheist, basing its atheism on a kind of negative faith which is sometimes scientific at bottom, but

[1] See *Why We Believe,* in this series.

which holds that its own want of beliefs cannot be scientifically justified; it is a relatively tolerant agnosticism, since the limitations of science are recognized and the denial of God is not absolutely required. Fairly close to this is a sort of religious sentimentalism which is rationalist in the field of science but professes a need for God in the realm of the emotional life. Of course, science and religion can be separated without reducing the latter to as little as that, and it is in this way that other fideist positions are produced. There are those, for example, who maintain that science is quite incapable of knowing or dealing with man as such, in his essence, and that there is a separate field which may or may not be rational belonging to religion. Or there are those who both grasp the rational explanations of science and hold firmly to their Catholic faith and accept its rational nature, yet go on making science and religion two separate worlds alongside of one another, without attempting to unite them and denying also the possibility of an apologetics based on science.

In the end we shall arrive at the right solution, the one way of looking at it which embraces the points of view of both science and religion, which can unite them while still drawing the necessary distinction in good, clear, philosophical terms. But there are in practice two ways of arriving at such a unity. First, there are some Christians who, in their enthusiasm in defence of the faith, try to prove conclusively that God exists from scientific premises; they either base their arguments on hypotheses, which are only provisional, and so achieve an agreement which is always threatened with destruction, or they rely on the "gaps" in science, which are no less provisional and are continually being filled. Such apologetics tries to convict the agnostic of being irrational on the scientific level itself, of not being willing to see facts which are really in some way experimental. Such idealist, "slanted" apologetics is not uncommon, and it is often very difficult to argue against it: one appears to be arguing against God. Yet we must argue against it, in the name of truth, if we want not simply to harry the agnostic, however justly, but to lead him to the beginnings of a real understanding of the possibility of the knowledge of God. True apologetics takes science for what it really is, and does not cling to what is only temporary in the scientific picture; it should draw out of science itself, by distinguishing various levels of apprehension and knowledge, ways of approach which suggest to the agnostic the true mystery of religion; it should show him that it is a possible rational hypothesis which the scientist can accept as in accord with all his scientific thinking. The door must be opened for him to philosophical argument, and to grace. On the other hand, for the Christian, who possesses a certainty in religion received from a different source, these approaches are wonderful ways in which science and metaphysics join together again in a perfect harmony which in a way verifies and confirms his faith.[2]

When we have set out this, the best, solution, it will be easy for us to show in conclusion the value of science as explanation, and to show also that it is not complete in itself but needs to be taken together with other forms of knowledge and explanation. We shall insist on the importance of philosophy as an autonomous way of knowing, which even when it has to rely on science loses none of its independence or of its own kind of certitude. This is something the modern world, bewildered by science and technology, has great difficulty in grasping; and this itself makes harder the acceptance of religion. If the modern Christian likes to find in his religion personal contact with Someone, it is nonetheless true that among the ordinary difficulties of life this contact might seem illusory, even when rationally based on revealed doctrine, unless it is supported by philosophical reflection on the reality described by science, which confirms for the Christian the existence of God the Creator. Nothing is more dangerous than to set over against one another personal religion and

[2] Where the Christian finds what almost amounts to proof which it would be unreasonable to reject, since, after all, he believes in God and knows him already, the agnostic can only find at most a likely possibility. Hence the different appearances of scientific apologetics, according as it is looked at from the point of view of the Christian or of the agnostic: the two must balance and limit one another.

scientific materialism. God must be found at the heart of matter itself.

Rémy Collin wrote that the thought of the scientist was thought born in the scientist in order that he might apprehend thought innate in things: the scientist receives the gift and the commission to pursue his research, to get to know God—in some small degree—in his creation. This is why, in the last resort, science is the impassioned search for God, for the justification of God, for a theodicy. It is up to scientists to contribute to human happiness by restoring to science its true appearance, lit by the reflection of the glory of God.

To work today for the reconciliation of science and religion is, as we shall see, to continue the great work of him in whom the Church has recognized her own true philosopher, St Thomas Aquinas. The agreement of his philosophy with modern scientific thought has been asserted, and rightly, by Fr Sertillanges and by Rémy Collin, and also by Teilhard de Chardin: "Transposed into a universe to which duration has added a new dimension, the theory of matter and form has become almost indistinguishable from our present speculations about the development of the natural world."

PART I

THE USE OF SCIENCE AGAINST
RELIGION

CHAPTER I

THE STORY OF A MISUNDERSTANDING: FROM DEMOCRITUS TO TEILHARD DE CHARDIN

The development of science as an independent field of knowledge, together with its technological consequences, which
have completely transformed the material conditions of human
life, is a comparatively recent phenomenon in the history of
man and his many civilizations. That development occurred
because of the extraordinary progress made by experimental
and applied science in the nineteenth century, thanks to the
work of scientists and engineers of various European nations.
It was this progress which enabled the white Europeans to
assert their ascendancy over the globe, the various parts of
which they were then "discovering". Even when these other
races and peoples set out to preserve their own culture, it is
by learning western science and technology that they now try
to achieve their independence and make up for their late
development. The problem of the relations between science
and religion has thus become a general one for all mankind,
which the missionary can no longer ignore, especially since
Marxism has increased its urgency and importance by treating
it as a political issue.

This sudden flowering of science and technology, which lies

behind the capitalist, colonial economy, was the work of men who had apparently no aptitudes superior to those of other races, but who were, through the Middle Ages and the Arabs and Byzantium, the inheritors of the rational thought of Greece, which itself continued the first scientific inquiries of the Egyptians and Babylonians. Greek thought was spread throughout the empire by Rome, and was then joined by Judaeo-Christian metaphysics, to produce western thought. The science of the ancient Mediterranean world did not differ fundamentally from other scientific beginnings elsewhere, in China or Pre-Columbian America, for example. Undeveloped as it was, it could hardly come into collision with religious ideas: physicists or naturalists, they were still philosophers. But some schools took more interest in science than others. This was obviously especially true of the first materialists such as Democritus and Lucretius, whose science was even then atheist; but it was also true of Aristotle, whose admirable scientific realism, especially in biology, was harmonized with a religious conception of the world. Very little progress was made in the Middle Ages. Theologians fitted the science of their time into their picture, and sometimes practised it, especially alchemy, though its association with magic was condemned. Albertus Magnus, Roger Bacon and Raymond Lull are examples of this union of science and religion. When the scientific philosophy of Aristotle, completed and perhaps altered by the thought of Arab (Averroës, Avicenna) or Jewish (Maimonides) philosophers, appeared to be dangerous for a faith developed in an idealist, Platonist tradition, St Thomas Aquinas succeeded in making his tremendous synthesis of scientific realism and Christian metaphysics. It is curious to see how few medieval men were interested in the physical world: taking no notice of real animals, they delighted in extraordinary descriptions of imaginary beasts which all had some mystical, symbolic significance.

Alas! St Thomas' system was so successful, that his successors, instead of carrying on his work as knowledge increased, fossilized it in a sterile scholasticism, divorced from this world, which was often mere word-play, more faithful to the letter than to the spirit of the Master.[1] And in addition, St Thomas, being like Aristotle in his lack of mathematics, established a philosophy very well suited to go along with progress in the biological sciences but closed to development in physics. This inability to accommodate the sciences of matter was aggravated by the misconceptions of matter fostered by the yet undeveloped physical sciences. So when the Renaissance came, many complex causes, including the return to antiquity, and the economic needs which drove explorers to undertake long sea voyages, led some thinkers to reject sterile argumentation in favour of experiment: know, in order to act. Leonardo da Vinci, scientist and philosopher of genius, and Francis Bacon, who taught the value of the experimental method, were precursors or contemporaries of the first stirrings of the revolution which was to change the world, the rise of modern science. Galileo, a great observer and experimenter, who had already corrected the wrong views of Aristotle on falling bodies, confirmed the hypothesis of Copernicus and Kepler in the face of tradition: the earth moves round the sun and is not at the centre of the universe. So the Bible must be wrong when it says that Joshua stopped the sun. Neither Galileo nor the Church was able to solve the dilemma, to make the distinction between the outlook of science and that of religion. The trial and condemnation of Galileo in 1616 marked the beginning of a tragic estrangement between science and religion. Theologians fell into regrettable error in their right and proper task of defending the faith. This became an important weapon in the arsenal of the anti-religious. In 1935, the most prominent exhibit in the anti-religious museum in Leningrad was a Foucault pendulum proving that the earth rotates on its axis. The same origin can be found for some of the recent statements about the anti-religious value of the sputniks, even though the case of Galileo has been properly settled for a long time.

[1] We should also notice the disastrous effect of *nominalism*, rationalist on the level of phenomena, fideist on that of religion.

Although many of these scientists were true Christians, their work destroyed the traditional background and context of religion and encouraged men not to accept anything simply on the word of Aristotle, but to verify everything for themselves, and so led many to extend their doubting to the whole teaching of the Church. Such were the seventeenth-century freethinkers, whose ambiguous attitude combined a brave and justifiable struggle against conformism and a wrong denial of essential truths and values. As early as 1553, the doctor, Michael Servetus, had been condemned by the Inquisition and then executed by Calvin for remaining true to his highly personal ideas on the Trinity. Scholastic theologians were tied to Aristotle's physics, close-bound by the system of St Thomas, and could not see that the new science had nothing to do with the faith. They were forced into greater mistrust of all things new by the Reformation, and tried in vain to resist the scientific revolution, which found unsuspected properties in matter and replaced the "spirits" which caused the revolution of the celestial spheres by the laws of gravitation.

The work of Descartes was even more disastrous for the future of relations between science and religion than the case of Galileo. Not because he thought that one should doubt everything not demonstrated as true by the reason; not because he was, as has wrongly been alleged, a concealed atheist; but because he opposed the Aristotelian and Thomist synthesis of soul and body in the unity of man by going back to the Platonic division: a spiritual soul acting at a particular point in the material body. For the first time, a fairly satisfactory description was given of the working of the nervous reflex in man and in the animals, and this was regarded as explaining completely the behaviour of animals as simply machines, but in the case of man the nervous system was used as an instrument by the spiritual soul. It was useless for La Fontaine to protest against this assimilation of animals to automata of the fountains in the king's gardens, rightly insisting on the animal soul, which St Thomas had so clearly shown to be similar to that of man. Down to the beginning of this century, the whole effort of philosophers in the eighteenth and physiologists in the nineteenth century was directed to disproving the existence of any direction of the brain by a separate spiritual soul and to showing that the material mechanisms of that organ were sufficient to explain thought. By separating the soul from the body, Descartes opened the door to materialism. It is a curious fact, but this idea, so opposed both to Thomist philosophy and to biblical metaphysics, seems to have been implicitly granted by many theologians, because it allowed them to keep apart the two fields, that of the body, reserved to science, and that of the soul, belonging wholly to religion.

Another great Catholic thinker and scientist-philosopher, Pascal, perhaps influenced by Jansenist pessimism, strictly opposed the two orders both in his thinking and in his life: the order of science and reason, and that of religious feeling and the heart, the truly Christian greatness of the order of charity which made it impossible for him to recognize spiritual values incarnate in other orders of reality. Like Descartes, and as unconsciously, he provided later rationalist critics with their arguments.

Alongside of this progress in experimental science, the materialist approach to the problem of knowledge by Hobbes and, especially, Locke, reduced ideas to sensations. By means of such theories the French eighteenth-century thinkers such as Condillac, Helvetius and Diderot, the first to produce a materialist synthesis based on science, discarded Descartes' dichotomy and reduced the spiritual principle to a property of the brain. This movement grew in strength with the progress of science and its applications (such as the perfecting of the steam engine by Watt), which then began transforming the material conditions of man's life, and cut at the root of all traditional religious ideas. In opposing it, more spiritual philosophers like Voltaire and Rousseau professed a more or less pantheist deism no less antipathetic to the Church.

In the nineteenth century science and technology made giant strides forward, especially in the fields of chemistry, based on Lavoisier's work, and of biology. No longer was it simply a matter of the curiosity of men of the world, of the arguments of philosophers: it became a fundamental characteristic of western civilization which offered men unheard-of new potentialities. Laplace taught a doctrine of universal determinism which seemed to make God unnecessary, since everything was bound together and explicable on the scientific level, everything was predictable if only all the causes were known. The idea of the earth and man as far more ancient than was compatible with tradition gradually gained ground and finally conquered in the mid-century with the discovery of fossil men and the publication of Darwin's theory of evolution: he even went so far as to declare that man was of the same descent as the animals. So man, no longer the centre of the universe, became merely a fully developed, perfectly evolved ape. Materialist philosophers went beyond what was properly scientific and drew anti-religious arguments from science. On the other hand theologians, disturbed by these new and as yet dubiously authenticated ideas, made no distinctions between what was scientific fact, what was theory, and what was philosophical or metaphysical interpretation.

At the same time, a philosophical doctrine, the positivism of Auguste Comte, systematized the new directive rule of science, making the age of science follow logically and historically after the ages of religion and of philosophy. Science, which was itself fast extending its domain, was given absolute competence in all human affairs: a religion of science was to take the place of the gods in the hearts of men. An anti-Christian revival of biblical scholarship, especially in Germany, endeavoured to strip the New Testament of any value as history: Jesus became either simply a great man or a myth. Saint-Simon, Littré, Renan and Taine became the high priests of science, and led to the triumph of scientific rationalism in the closing years of the century with the biologist-philosopher Haeckel and the chemist Berthelot. True, the greatest scientists of the age adopted a more sensible and objective attitude: Bernard and Pasteur, though not Catholics, refused to support materialism. But the first could not, as a scientist, accept Descartes' separation of the spiritual from the physical, yet ignored, as did his contemporaries, the true, Thomist solution which was in fact so close to his own. And the second reduced religion to a sentimental consolation having nothing to do with science. The revival of a true Christian faith among many thinking men—including some scientists—did not achieve a synthesis of science and religion. Voltaire's middle classes, following Napoleon I, saw in religion the means of defending their privileges, which they regarded as God's rewards for their own merits.

So scientific positivism thought in its utopian optimism that the development of science and education would be enough automatically to ensure man's happiness by making a reality such an atheist ideal society as Zola describes in *Work*. But another materialist theory was being developed, wholly directed to political ends, which meant to achieve by the revolution of the oppressed proletariat not only the happiness of man and the advancement of knowledge but the disappearance of religion. Karl Marx and his friend Friedrich Engels fitted themselves into the movement of thought of the nineteenth century, making use of Darwinism and atheist exegetics. Engels, in his *Dialectics of Nature,* sketched a biological philosophy which should include man. But the chief distinction of Marxism is that it was the third revolution, after Galileo and Darwin, to pull man down from his throne: the spiritual and cultural development of man is the fruit of his labour, and thus bound up with economic conditions; so religion appears as a sort of alienation of man, preventing him from working towards his liberation.

The deficiencies of scientific materialism which Marxism itself exposed; the failure of premature attempts at all-embracing, all-explaining syntheses; the fact that science itself has challenged positions believed to be firmly established; and the dream of contentment which ended in social struggles and international wars: all these things have profoundly changed the relations between science and religion in the twentieth century. Scientists have learned that their science is incomplete and that care must be exercised not to extrapolate too far: has not the face of physics itself completely altered, with quanta, relativity, nuclear physics and the arguments over determinism? Each science has its own proper field, but all of human life is not necessarily accessible to science. At the same time theologians, stimulated by the revival of Thomism in the Church (Cardinal Mercier, Pope Leo XIII), and using the contribution of philosophers like Bergson and Maritain, are no longer content to seem to give way to science, stubbornly defending unchangeable traditional positions: they have learnt to distinguish what belongs to science from what belongs to religion, what is unchanging from what can change with the progress of science because it is only the context in which the faith is incarnate. This is a difficult task in which care is needed but where too much caution can stand in the way of the Church's apostolate. So we have passed from the atheist science of the beginning of the century, so irreconcilable with religion, to a more or less tolerantly neutral agnosticism which leaves room for religion if it will keep to its proper place. For Christian scientists this corresponds to Grasset's famous distinction between the oratory and the laboratory, which must not be confused: they are two strictly separate compartments of life[2]—the rational life of the scientist, and the ordinary life of man supported by religion. There is no real relationship between the physical, scientific explanation of the sequence and interrelations of minute events, the "how" (and its technological and practical consequences), and metaphysical, philosophical reflection on the meaning of the world or of man, on first causes, the "why". The usefulness of science is recognized, but it does not automatically advance towards good: it can be dangerous, it can lead mankind by various paths to its doom. It all depends on how men use their science, basing their actions on moral precepts having nothing to do with science. Above all, in this atomic age in which biological science claims more and more of man for its own,

[2] The Modernist struggle has caused the brave attempts at a synthesis made by some Catholic scientists at the end of the nineteenth century to be forgotten.

optimism has given place to a pessimism which makes men stand in fear of the baneful advance of science.

This return to a pessimistic agnosticism which results from the apparent check given to three centuries of scientific and technological advance can, however, only be a temporary crisis, out of which even now are coming the beginnings of a solution in two mutually opposed ways. Marxism, based on a now more realistic scientific conception of the world, and having shed many of the errors of the old mechanistic materialism, today takes over from scientific atheism in conditions which call for a renewal of spiritual apologetics; it too predicts for mankind a happiness built on science and technology, thanks to the automatic progress of history. Marxism has gained its great political power from the whole movement of revolt among the poor, whose rightful place in society has been denied to them by a capitalist civilization. So it has become a brooding menace to the future of Christianity, threatening not only persecution but, even worse, an anti-religious system of education based on omniscient science, imposed on pupils denied the possibility of acquiring a truly religious background.

In the face of Marxism, and also in the face of modern science, which is now itself establishing a new philosophical view of man and the world which does not ignore human and spiritual values, or at any rate no longer denies them as did the old scientific rationalism, but tries to explain them, it is no longer enough to cling to a spiritual reality divorced from the world which is the specific field of religion. After Galileo, Darwin and Marx comes Freud, to strip from man his last privilege: are not his consciousness and his freedom only illusions concealing the determinism of an all-powerful unconscious, in which religious values lose all their reality? Is not sin simply a morbid and false culpability of which the doctor and the mind-manipulator can relieve us by freeing us from our complexes, making us automatically good—that is, conformable?

The older rationalism asked too much of an as yet undeveloped science; contemporary science, even if it is still developing, supplies us with a sufficient basis for this new, all-embracing rationalism, which Marxism tends to become. The scientist's idea of the universe is going to seek out the Christian in his private corner: he will have to come out and face it confidently, distinguishing the two different aspects, the religious and the scientific, of his conception of the world, and he must bear witness that these are but two aspects of the same reality, not contradictory at all. So he must assert the existence of natural values common to the Christian and the agnostic. If mankind is to survive and go forward, if we are to escape a nuclear holocaust and the breakdown into anarchy of all standards and values, and the destruction of freedom by totalitarianism, then Christians and non-Christians must work together in reconciliation to extract from the scientific account of the world an idea of man which shall establish standards. If, in the spirit of St Thomas Aquinas, bypassing the mistake of Descartes, "the phenomenon of man" and the "divine *milieu*" can come together again, we may find the means to build a new synthesis, to return to the true Judaeo-Christian metaphysics of the Old Testament and St Paul, a metaphysics now built into the context of the scientific description and explanation of the world, of which it is itself the supreme Explanation. "I am convinced", wrote Teilhard de Chardin,[3] "that the two points of view require to be brought into union, and that they will soon unite in a kind of phenomenology or generalized physics in which the internal aspect of things as well as the external aspect of the world will be taken into account. Otherwise, so it seems to me, it is impossible to cover the totality of the cosmic phenomenon by one coherent explanation such as science must try to construct." If all this can be done, in accordance with what the Church has always taught, then there can be no conflict between science and religion except when the two are confused.

[3] Teilhard de Chardin, *The Phenomenon of Man* (Eng. trans., Collins, London, and Harper & Bros., New York, 1959), p. 53.

CHAPTER II

MECHANISTIC RATIONALISM

CONTEMPORARY RATIONALISM

Despite the present importance of Marxist materialism, which notwithstanding its atheism keeps something of the appeal of a religion, we must be careful not to think of the old rationalist materialism of sixty years ago as simply of historical interest. Many of our materialist contemporaries, and especially many scientists, even if they reject Marxism, still profess a scientific materialism more realistic than the older rationalism but no less atheist. If some of them only go so far as a careful agnosticism, basing their non-belief in God on science but not asserting his non-existence as proved, others are wholly convinced that the idea of God is incompatible with scientific thinking. They often express an equal horror for religious ideas and for Marxism: the latter they oppose as being equally totalitarian and illiberal, since for them science leads only to what is contingent and relative, providing no fixed standards and no sense of direction in history. We can quote, for example, Bertrand Russell and his book on *Science and Religion*, the Viennese school of neo-positivists, or logical positivists, for whom all metaphysics is merely illogical word-play (for example, A. J. Ayer in his book, *Language, Truth and Logic*), and scientists like Julian Huxley with his *New Humanism*.

For such rationalist atheists, whose detailed philosophical positions need not be analysed here, there is no mystery, no Unknowable. The frontiers of the unknown are continually being pushed back by the advance of scientific knowledge. Such is the only rational kind of knowledge; its truth is authenticated by the control it gives to men, which enables them to act effectively. Of such human knowledge we can be rightly proud. But this pride in being active and thinking should be balanced by a humble recognition of our own condition: we are but swiftly passing products of a universe which is completely without reason and inhuman, in which we are localized at an insignificantly tiny point. Science will destroy religion. The struggle against religion is a duty, since religion teaches things which are false and incompatible with science, the remnants of an age of ignorance. Religion incurably deforms the mind of man by encouraging its irrationality, by imposing its dogmas upon it; by its intolerance and its fanaticism it prevents understanding between men; and it tries to halt the advance of science.

We must now examine in more detail these various uses of science made by atheist rationalism. In doing so we must be careful not to conclude either that this is indeed the true objective import of science, or that these ideas are altogether false.

RATIONALIST SCIENTIFIC EXPLANATION

For everything which happens outside himself, primitive man tends to invoke an anthropomorphic explanation, attributing events to a will like his own, to the intervention of hidden spirits. He is an animist and sees gods or spirits everywhere; he can, by reflection, distinguish his own mind or soul from his body. He regards himself as the centre of the universe, the object of the special attention of the gods, and of demons, with whom he establishes a relationship through magic. Everything is possible, and with his pre-logical mind he believes in the reality of dreams and in action at a distance. His longing not to disappear into nothingness leads him to the cult of the dead and belief in his own soul's immortality. Later, religious feeling is more purified, and God, the supreme giver of life, delegates his powers to spiritual principles such as vital force: vitalism succeeds animism.

Now the scientific description appears to replace all such dualistic explanations by a strict monism: there are only those properties of matter which our senses perceive. When any phenomenon occurs, it is only necessary to discover the cause and the phenomenon is reproducible at will. The old determinism of Laplace oversimplified things: the world is too complex, too un-human, for us to be able to know it entirely, but it nevertheless consists solely of natural, material phenomena. Experience and reason together enable us to understand it all. Miracles, contrary to the laws of nature, are impossible. They must be only illusions based on bad observation or suggestion. True, physics has changed. We have learned to see, behind electro-magnetic phenomena and so on, the reality of the particles and waves of matter and energy whose behaviour makes up the world. The indeterminism which some religious philosophers have wanted to use as a proof of the world's irrationality simply shows the difficulty of making observations when we get so far from the human scale of things; it has nothing to do with free will. Moreover, a better understanding of the facts considerably reduces the philosophical importance of that indeterminism. We may even now be on the verge of discovering the theory or the equation sought for by Einstein, to give a unified explanation of all phenomena. The universe is comprehensible and describable in mathematical terms, and this impersonal abstraction, seemingly so far removed from reality, is the source of all atomic energy. It is wrong to describe the world as like a machine; it is a complex material whole in which each event seems to happen in isolation simply by virtue of the properties of matter.

Science, in making material phenomena known to us, has removed all idea of spirit from the world of the inanimate, the world of atomic or astronomic physics. Now it seems to be doing the same for the world of life and thought. Life is not a mysterious force or specific kind of energy: it results from the properties of living matter. This is only a highly complex sort of matter which biochemists hope one day soon to be able to synthesize in the laboratory, reproducing the process that once happened, millions of years ago, in the primitive seas in which life was born out of inanimate matter. It is true that the difficulties have sometimes been underestimated, and mistakes have been made; much more progress in the chemistry of proteins will be needed before living matter is artificially manufactured, and perhaps it will never be done; but that will not be for theoretical reasons but because the technical difficulties are too great. The beginnings of life must have required millions of years of increasing complexity in pre-living organic matter. In the living being there are no elements other than those of inorganic matter, no forms of energy other than those known elsewhere. The whole has, it is true, a considerable degree of organization and complexity, but this is no less a property of matter. When the conditions of the environment are unfavourable to the organism, it decays, and that is death. Like every heat machine, the living organism is a transformer of energy leaving a residue of unusable heat.

Every living organism can be observed to have a pattern of behaviour which represents objectively its level of "mental" development. Even the lowliest organisms, unicellular creatures like the amoeba, display fairly complicated reaction patterns. Now these can be explained in terms of the properties of organic matter, as Loeb showed when he discovered that animal tropisms, like those of plants, are due to the action of physico-chemical factors in the environment on the complex structures of the cell. It has now been realized that these tropisms are much more complicated than Loeb thought in his over-simplified mechanistic theory, but this does not alter the fact that their very complexity is a property of the protoplasm which contains the germ of all the behaviour of higher organisms. If their behaviour is still more complicated, if they can adapt themselves better to new circumstances in the environment, this is because their organization is more complex, their nervous system more developed. Thus, they have instincts, which are not mysterious metaphysical entities taking the place of intelligence, but built-in aptitudes to react in a reflex manner to certain stimuli in the environment. As well as instinct, the development of the nervous system introduces the possibility of conditioning certain reflexes, of producing new reactions. The integration of the nervous system makes it possible for the higher animals to integrate their instincts and conditioned reflexes sufficiently to have a certain control over them, and thus intelligence emerges. It used to be fashionable either to attribute human feelings to animals, or to oppose animal and man, animals being mere automata. Science has now shown that men and animals are similar beings, man only differing in that his brain is so much more highly complex.

The progress made in neurophysiology has reduced the mind to an apparently useless hypothesis. It has never been discovered under the scalpel, and for a long time now physiologists have thought that psychological life can be explained in terms of the working of the brain. The great hope of localizing all the various psychological functions in different regions of the brain has now vanished: psychological phenomena are not materially produced or localizable. The brain is only the seat of psychological phenomena; thought seems to be the functional aspect of the brain working as a whole. Besides, science is only concerned with behaviour: so, for science, the brain is the organ for directing behaviour. Such an objective study has no need to take account of subjective self-consciousness or conscience. These are only metaphysical notions belonging to another order than the phenomenological; they are an illusion which can be neglected, at least unless and until the advance of neurophysiology enables us to understand how they arise. For the most up-to-date materialists consciousness is no longer a taboo, it is a phenomenon, a property of the brain, and its rudiments are to be found in the higher animals. To suppose in these conditions that the mind can survive the body's death, and therefore the death of the brain, is completely irrational: at death, everything stops.

Thanks to his brain, man is undeniably superior to other animals, but he is merely an animal, evolved to perfection. Part of his superiority is derived, what is more, from his cultural and social life: at the start he was most like an anthropoid ape (a chimpanzee). Within the framework of the theory of evolution, which alone accounts for the development of progressively more complex life on earth, we now know that if man did not descend from the ape, properly speaking, at least men and apes have common ancestors. The genetic mutation, that is, the sudden change, which produced man, consisted above all in the acquisition of a bigger brain, which was made possible by the modification of his skull, which was itself the result of his upright stance. We know now some of the intermediate species which have disappeared: upright-standing anthropoids such as the Australopithecines of South Africa, for example, or forerunners such as Java man or Pekin man, fossils marking the change towards man, whether Neanderthal man-beast or man proper (*homo sapiens*, Cro-Magnon man). It is not really possible to know which among these creatures can properly be called man. What criterion can we adopt? The volume of the brain, toolmaking, the use of fire, the cult of the dead or the art of magic? So, man appeared on the earth by the same processes and mechanisms as produced other species; perhaps he is not even the last product of evolution?

This evolution is a material process with nothing supernatural about it; so it seems to be opposed to the idea of God the Creator. Now it is certainly impossible today to hold to a naïve "creationism". We may not know precisely how evolution works, or worked in the past, but the fact of evolution is incontestable. Some good evolutionary biologists think that mutations happen by chance, and that it is the natural selection of the fittest which brings about the observable harmony of adaptations and of more and more complex characteristics. In the same way, the development of each creature from the embryo is not governed by any mysterious spiritual force or according to any pre-established plan, but depends on the interaction of its hereditary genetic make-up and the environment. Many things are still unknown, but nothing is inexplicable. Science will soon account for what we do not yet know. When we understand the physical world a little better, we shall be able to account for all that exists in the universe:

the less will contain the greater in itself, and spirit will be seen to be phenomenologically second in respect to matter, which gives birth to it.

THE ABSURDITY OF THE WORLD

A ridiculous little atom, lost in an unfeeling and infinite universe, man knows that his feverish activity is only a tiny local phenomenon, ephemeral, meaningless, aimless. He knows that his values are valid only for him; he knows that for the universe of the galaxies and the stars the fall of an empire or of an ideal is of no more significance than the crushing of an ants' nest under the heedless foot of a passer-by. There is nothing else for him to do but try to forget the brute immensity that crushes him without even noticing. Thrusting down a sickening but pointless fear of the infinite, deaf to the terrifying silence of space, he tries to become as unnatural as nature is inhuman. Forced grimly back on himself, he dedicates himself in a humble, earthly fashion to the realization of his own paltry plans, to which he pretends to attach as much importance as if they really had some relevance to eternal purposes.

So J. Rostand on man. And this is the second aspect of rationalist atheism. If it expects everything of science and exalts man, yet it recognizes humbly that this human creature who can do so little is, at bottom, nothing. He has appeared by chance at a particular point in an immense and meaningless universe, and he will end, all humanity will end, in nothingness. His work is bound, on any account, to be futile. All we can do is try to be happy in forgetting this and working for the happiness of others. The revolt against a meaningless cosmos can lead, as Camus showed, to brotherly solidarity.

One might, at first sight, be tempted to use science in order to understand, to discover a meaning, a purpose, in the universe, or at least in this corner of the universe where we have been evolved. But this would be to confuse a result with a purpose. It is true that man is the result, the end-product, of a process of evolution; but nothing entitles us to say that he is the end aimed at, the purpose of evolution. Because a genetic mutation, it may be purely a chance mutation, threw up a "sport" in the progeny of some early primate, a "sport" which, it turned out, was better fitted for the struggle for survival, we are not entitled to conclude that this happened in order that man should come to be. Because the function of the eye is to see, are we entitled to say that it was made for seeing, or was developed for that purpose? The chance possession of a pigment, which by the increasing complexity of its evolutionary development became an eye, simply gave a tremendous advantage to the possessor. Our eye is not made for seeing: we see because we have an eye.

Simply because chance and the physico-chemical laws of matter have led to the appearance of man on earth, we cannot infer anything sure about the origin, present state, or future of the universe. Did it have a beginning, or does it change continuously, cyclically, eternally? Is it ever-expanding? Are there any limits to it? Are there any other living things like us on other planets in other systems? We must wait for the astronauts to go and see. But it seems quite likely to be so: the earth is not specially privileged. There is nothing but the purposeless and incoherent transformation of matter and energy; all that we see is the transitory successes of this blind process, that is, those things which are lucky enough to have a sufficiently adapted organization of their parts to be able to continue in existence. Man is one such success; a remarkable success, thanks to the properties of his nervous system, but as ephemeral, as meaningless, as the rest, even if he alone senses the insensibility of the world, even if he alone is afraid of death. And this very consciousness, is it really, if we reject an outmoded anthropocentrism, is it really an objective sign of man's superiority? Is it really an advantage to have to work out what to do instead of relying on instincts automatically adapted to the normal environment? As an organism, man is relatively simple compared with the extraordinary creatures which have been developed in the plant and animal kingdoms. The most unlikely creatures have been evolved, even absurd and nonsensical ones, the very characteristics of which make life impossible. How can this petty creature man, the chance product of evolution, be the centre of the universe, the object of the special care of a Creator God?

Man imagines himself free and responsible; he must obey the voice of conscience, which tells him what is right and what is wrong. Does not modern science show us that this too is a dangerous illusion leading to fanaticism and intolerance? His freedom is merely apparent: are we free to be lazy or active, when this depends on the working of the thyroid or the adrenal gland? Are we responsible for our hereditary constitution, our chromosomes and genes? Psycho-analysis shows us as entangled in a mesh of determinisms: what we think is a free decision is motivated by some unknown cause in the unconscious, which is the sublimation or the repression of some feeling which cannot be outwardly expressed because the super-ego of social constraint will not allow it. Even the most innocent of our slips has some hidden cause. The idleness of a child is really his hidden jealousy towards his younger brother, and so on. There is no more need for useless worry and advice: we have only to cure the sickness of which bad behaviour is the symptom. As for constraints in the moral order, these are clearly entirely relative. We think good what accords with our nature (is a pervert to blame if he is not as other people?) and especially what we have learned is good, from all our environment. We are prisoners of custom and conformity, and setting ourselves free is often really only exchanging our fetters for those of the opposing system, of the non-conformist, or of him who rejects all constraints and all obligations. All customs are changeable, varying in time and space from culture to culture, from class to class. Knowledge, however, is surely a source of freedom? I know now why I do things, what determines my actions; so I am more free than if I imagined that I did only what I wanted to do while really being completely enslaved. To some degree, we learn to choose from what is determined that which is most suitable—but suitable to what, if not to what we judge to be good because of other determining causes? The seeking of our own pleasure, for example, or the general good of others. This freedom so gratuitously asserted

by Gide and Sartre is fundamentally as nonsensical as the whole
condition of man. But because it makes possible action directed
to the betterment of life, we must preserve it as if it were true
liberty. We must struggle to lessen all external oppressions
enforced in the name of authority, of the State or of a Church.
The individual must determine himself, without adding to his
own determinants any outside constraint. The moral restraints
which religion would impose on us are merely devices for
mystification, making absolute certain complexes of primitive
man: so Jungian psycho-analysis, after Freud. The moralist is
often a Pharisee, an orthodox conformist: that is, a man full of
repressions. Obviously some rules are needed for social life, and
it is this practical minimum of purely secular morality which
ought to be taught to the young. But it has no other basis than
the pragmatic one. Education must avoid enforcing restraints
which, by repressing natural instincts, are the source of psychological disorders. Produced as he is by accident, by chance, man
is certainly far from perfection. Happily, the advance of science
offers the hope of improvement, of making a superman, more
intelligent and—who knows?—perhaps capable of living, if not
for ever, at least for very much longer. Much can be expected
from eugenics or from the cure and prevention of organic and
nervous disorders. But we must not forget that we are only
"sorcerer's apprentices" who may, wanting to improve a nonsensical nature, make it still more nonsensical.

REASON AGAINST RELIGION

The only attitude which is truly rational and worthy of
modern man is to accept only what can be seen; or rather, since
our senses often deceive us and common sense is prone to make
mistakes, to trust only scientific analysis of physical reality.
Setting aside the assertions of theologians that belief is rational,
the rationalist atheist declares that credence cannot be given to
verbal constructions supposed to correspond to realities which
are not material and so cannot be known by any of the senses.
Religion is a pre-scientific way of explaining things, produced

by primitive man, who imagined himself the centre of the universe and felt in need of protection. Now, when science, in understanding and explaining the universe, has put mind in its proper place as emerging from the operation of physical causes, there is no longer any need to call on the aid of spiritual realities which explain nothing and are never perceived by scientific methods. More, science actually disproves their existence by describing the universe as autonomous and meaningless: it is not a world controlled by Providence, in which all is put at the service of man by the magical intervention of God, who can even answer our prayers by working miracles. Why pray for healing or for rain, when medicine cures and irrigation waters?

Christianity has taught irrational beliefs, opposed to science; it has always opposed the progress of science, ever since its beginnings in Galilee; it has persecuted and executed many a liberal spirit; it is a totalitarian fanaticism. It has given way before the advance of science, but it still profits from the unknown in order to affirm the Unknowable. It seems now to have left science in occupation of the field, claiming that it has its own proper sphere. But even if this is better, this sphere remains a non-existent myth. If the Church became powerful again, under the appearances of toleration she would again oppose freedom of inquiry and research. Can we not see this now in her cautious reticence in the face of the theory of the evolution of man, whom she splits into a physical body and a spiritual soul, which requires the intervention of God but which is of no advantage to the animal? How can we reconcile the idea of Adam, perfect and immortal, incapable of suffering, whose nature, and the nature of all whose descendants, was corrupted by original sin, with the scientific picture of primitive man as a savage? According to Christianity this world which we love in spite of its lack of meaning is a place of exile, a vale of tears, a place of punishment in expectation of eternal happiness, for which men must suffer or wait in resignation: for why do anything, if prayer is effective and if our present life has no real value?

If the worst comes to the worst the illusory comforts of

religion can be allowed to those who are neither brave nor clear-thinking enough to bear the pains of life and the expectation of death. But such religion must keep its place, and not impose on men's minds irrational dogmas, not busy itself with science and the explanation of the world, not pervert the mind irreparably with its fairy tales. The fight against Catholicism in the cause of science and such freedom as man has is for the rationalist atheist not only a duty, the duty of the scientist to fight against ignorance; it is a matter of cleansing and healing the mind of man. Religion, which was once responsible for the hysterical performances of wizards and sorcerers, whom it then racked and burned, now leads feeble minds, especially women, into psychiatric disorders: diabolic possession, the hallucinations of self-styled mystics, stigmatizations, prolonged fasting—these are but the half-unconscious deceits of foolish women. All these things point to the survival, through religion, of phenomena which will be swept away as science and reason advance. As to the origin of Christianity, atheist criticism has sifted out what is historical a long time ago, and shown how the myth developed and its similarities to other ancient religions.

If the rationalist and scientific atheist is now more realistic about the true potentialities of science, which is far from being able to know it all, and if he has lost a good deal of his optimism concerning the future happiness of mankind guided by science alone, his polemic has lost none of its anti-religious virulence. We shall reply to it step by step in the second and third parts of this book: though the whole of this series replies to it in a sense, by giving a true picture of the faith.[1] It is relatively easy to answer his objections, for we are dealing with a materialism which, although it recognizes the notion—as yet unworked-out philosophically—of increasing complexity of organization, yet treats what is superior as a function of what is inferior, and so considerably debases human and spiritual

---

[1] See especially the books in section III of this series, particularly Rémy Collin, *Evolution: Hypotheses and Problems*, and René Biot, *What is Life?*

values. The picture of the world and man thus presented to us can justly be accused of falling short of what is needed, but this does not necessarily imply, as an over-simple apologetics might think, that religion is necessary for the defence of these values, since it is still not proved that they are completely excluded, by definition, from the competence of science. But either science is as yet not sufficiently developed to include them in its scope, or materialism misrepresents science in order to remove all values from it. We are now going to examine in detail a scientific philosophy of greater importance, Marxism, although it also is false to true scientific objectivity in that it clings to some remnants of the old mechanistic rationalism.

CHAPTER III

ATHEIST REALISM AND MARXIST DIALECTICS

THE IMPORTANCE OF MARXISM

Why is Marxism important?[1] How has a philosophy dating from the middle of the last century come to have such great political power? Why, despite its totalitarianism, is it so attractive to minds which ought, since they call themselves progressive, to be firm advocates of freedom? Why have many scientists in all fields professed themselves Marxists, asserting not only that science leads inevitably to Marxism—if they are not one and the same—but also that Marxist methods are to their own advantage, enabling them to be better scientists than if they had stuck to the older rationalism? Why is Marxism atheist? Is this an additional aspect, or really an essential element in its teaching?

Some people talk of Marxism as a new religion, atheist, but dogmatic; others think of it as a political doctrine, the seizure of dictatorial power in the service of the oppressed masses; for others again, it is essentially a science, a way of thinking, the analysis of the machinery of economics and social life in the past and the future. Then there are those who stress the philosophical character of Marxism, against those who see in it *the* scientific picture of man and the world. All this is only apparently contradictory. Marxism is an idea of man and the world based on the analysis of the various fields of reality made

---

[1] We are here concerned with the scientific aspect only; for a more complete study see E. Borne, *Modern Atheism* and H. Chambre, S.J., *The Church and Communism.* in this series.

by the various sciences; among these the social sciences and economics are especially cultivated and developed; but for full understanding and for action, the Marxist must rise to the level of scientific philosophy which explains and accounts for everything. So Marxism is a sort of scientific rationalism, according to which nothing falls outside the competence of science. It is a very different kind of rationalism from the old mechanistic sort. Far from reducing what is superior to what is inferior, the Marxist dialectic of nature gives man his place at the summit of living things, and asserts his special superiority. But it is like the older rationalism in that it considers this superiority as purely material in origin, even if it is manifested at the level of mind. The world is not meaningless, but its history and biological evolution have an aim, the production of man. Man does not naturally and immediately possess consciousness and freedom: in the beginning he is almost a mere animal, and only gradually forms his consciousness of self and his freedom by means of social life and communal work. Mental life is a superstructure built on social and economic life. The knowledge of the laws which govern the direction of history allow man to undertake the construction of the "new man", the citizen of a just and classless society in which happiness reigns. As opposed to scientific rationalism, Marxism does not devalue human life: it does not make man simply a highly evolved animal. Or rather, it confesses that his high degree of evolution has brought about a change in his nature. But the human values of the Marxist are not a natural part of man; they are added to the individual from outside through social relationships. Self-consciousness is a consequence of membership of a society. So all the deviations of the self are simply consequences or reflections of social disorders: achieve the just society and the self finds its proper balance and harmony, and sin becomes impossible. It is therefore right that the individual self, recognizing that it is nothing without society, should submit wholly to the orders of those who make the new society and the new man.

So it is no longer in the cause of science that religion is condemned, in the name of the autonomy of an evolving world.

It is done in the name of a self-styled scientific criticism which makes of religion the alienation of man produced by economic oppression. To bear life at all, man projects into a myth his ideals of power and freedom: he can never become man in a full sense again unless he takes back the attributes he gave to God and ceases to resign himself to his lot. So Marxism is doubly and essentially atheist: an atheism which is bound up with the construction of the new man is infinitely more compelling than the atheism of the older rationalist, who is only concerned to see man set free from the old bonds of dogma by his reason. Yet since mental life depends on social and economic factors, anti-religious propaganda is of only secondary importance. Whereas the rationalist knows he must fight to make religion disappear, the Marxist is simply certain that without his doing anything, provided capitalism is got rid of and the new economic society is developed, religion will necessarily disappear, even if only after some delay. So it can be tolerated for a time as a regrettable but unimportant personal, private choice.

That Marxism is essentially anti-religious is obvious, and this makes it intrinsically wrong, for the Christian. However, the way in which it attacks religion, with new arguments ostensibly drawn from science added to the old ones, necessitates a new and specially adapted apologetics. It is not enough to assert human values, for these the Marxist recognizes, after a fashion, though radically opposing them in a religious context, since, according to the Marxist, religion alienates and debases them. Marxism can hardly be blamed for drawing from science, as the older scientific rationalism did not, a fairer picture of man. Since, in Marxism, human values are given a material explanation capable of being absorbed into a materialist metaphysics, it is not enough simply to assert them in the service of religion. They must be fully described in all those aspects which Marxism, because of the deficiencies of its materialism, cannot perceive on the scientific level. Marxism is a close-knit whole, but the Christian must distinguish in it what is objective scientific fact or accepted theory, and what is only metaphysical inference, not strictly a consequence of science. Among the objective facts of science which Marxism insists on are some important ones of which religion must take account if it is to retain its full value at the present time: some out-of-date expressions which contradict scientific knowledge and which are used to calumniate religion must be done away with. The situation today is very similar to that in the thirteenth century. Aristotelianism was a philosophy based on scientific realism and so possessing some permanent value; but some deductions from it were opposed to Catholic theology. St Thomas Aquinas was able to preserve the truths of Aristotelianism while correcting the errors, which were by no means necessary consequences but depended on the point of view—although Aristotle himself might not have resigned himself to their rejection. The refutation of Marxist atheism must not therefore obscure the fact that Marxism may have some scientific roots which must not be destroyed along with the strictly non-scientific metaphysical interpretation which Marxism grafts on to them. The atheism of the Marxist is doubtless more essential and more profound than that of the old scientific rationalist: but in his idea of a world arranged in order and ordered to an end he is very much nearer to the Christian idea than the other was.

While Catholics and non-Marxist rationalists can sometimes agree as to the dangers of Marxist totalitarianism, there can also be some agreement between the criticisms used by Catholics and Marxists against the errors of mechanistic rationalism, with its devaluation of man. It is true that Marxism only opposes the spirituality of religion, which it identifies with idealism; but it has many times declared that although it is taking over from the older rationalism it nonetheless intends to correct the old mistakes, and this battle against the old mechanistic rationalism is a distinct and important aspect of Marxist thinking. What makes Marx's dialectical materialism atheist, apart from his reflection on a theology he never understood, is his desire to explain how Christianity, to judge from the behaviour of Christians, seems to be so easily able to accommodate itself to the frightful social injustices consequent upon the rise of capitalism.

The best reply to Marxist atheism must therefore always be for Christians to undertake the building of the just society: this would prove wrong the Marxist interpretation of religion as the alienation of man, it would show that the nature of man is such that, in any given society or within any religious faith, his behaviour is still free, he can still do good or evil. To follow Marxism in attributing all evil to capitalism and all good to Communism, automatically, and to condemn Christianity because Christians go wrong, would be—as would the contrary attitude—to mistake the nature of man and his freedom.

ANTI-METAPHYSICAL DIALECTICS

For the Marxist, materialism is simply the scientific explanation of the universe; but it is not enough to call oneself materialist to be truly scientific. The advances of science in the nineteenth century, especially the biological sciences, rendered obsolete one way of being materialist. In this scientific realism, Marxism is not content simply to carry on the earlier materialist thought, from Democritus to Diderot. To the word "materialism" the Marxist adds an essential adjective: dialectical. This makes the Marxist the heir of a different philosophical tradition beginning with Heraclitus and ending in Hegel, which was not in any way materialist. Marx's originality lay in his borrowing Hegel's dialectics and turning Hegelianism upside down, "setting it on its feet again", by putting it to use in reviving a materialism which is thus brought more into agreement with scientific realism, and made more receptive to trends in scientific progress. He criticized the old materialism as mechanistic: since it was developed alongside of the advancement of science consequent upon the discovery of the laws of mechanics, at a time when the other sciences were still in their infancy, it thought of the world as a vast and relatively simple machine, men and animals being also machines. Organic matter was assimilated to inorganic, and mind was a material production of the brain. For Descartes, mind or spirit was a specific element acting from without on the body, which was material and simply a machine. For the mechanistic materialist, there was only this machine, and the importance of spirit dwindles as it comes to be thought of as simply a product of the working of the machine. He took no account of the extremely complex conditions needed for the development of mind. He refused to see that if life obeys the laws of physics and chemistry, and if thought does depend on the working of the brain, nevertheless living and thinking are in themselves specifically new processes. And even if he recognized the material complexity underlying life and thought, it was not given its proper philosophical importance. Along with his assimilation of the superior to the inferior went a mentality essentially closed to the ideas of development or history, a mind looking on the world as static or as moving in a perpetual circle on the same spot, with no advance. Consequently, when science began to develop its ideas on biological evolution, the fact of evolution was accepted, but it was deliberately denied all direction, any idea of progress. This refusal to see any meaning or purpose in natural processes led the old-fashioned materialist to minimize the part played by human action, by the changing of nature and of himself by man.

By calling his materialism dialectical, the Marxist gives prime importance to change itself, to the interconnections of all changes and the complexity of the causes which produce them. There is not one straight chain of causes and effects, but a multitude of mutual interactions. Everything acts on everything else, and we must be careful not to isolate one element from its context. Again, the Marxist dialectics is historical, insisting on the importance of the time factor. Change and movement are not circular, but spiral: that is, they have a direction. Now the Marxist sees reality as essentially contradictory, but far from denying any part of reality in order to remove the contradiction, it has to be overcome in a synthesis which will give their proper place to elements which are apparently contradictory. Things change because they contain internal contradictions of which the change is the resolution. Change is not gradual or progressive: as the resolution of contradictions it causes truly new qualities to appear, but these are only the consequence of an increase in quantitative complexity. The more comes from the less, not because there is nothing new in the more, but because the nature of the less changes in some way by becoming more complex, since quantity brings quality into being.

This philosophy of the autodynamism of change is not atheist simply because it endeavours to be scientifically materialist, getting rid of a useless God who cannot be observed. As a method of realist thinking, it tends to oppose very strongly what it considers to be the inverse of dialectics, metaphysics: both the metaphysics which according to the Marxist is implicit in mechanistic materialism, and that idealist metaphysics with which he identifies all spiritual philosophies. Marxists perfectly understand the possibility, and even the necessity, of separating materialism from mechanistic rationalism; but they will not admit the possibility of a spiritualist dialectics which is just as consistent with scientific realism. For them, any spiritual philosophy is a form of idealism, more or less related to the extreme form of Berkeley's philosophy, denying material reality. All metaphysics is necessarily anti-scientific: it denies change, asserts identity, isolates individual things, makes eternal and insuperable divisions everywhere, sets countries against one another, and has a horror of contradiction. In his perfectly just criticism of this sort of metaphysics, Hegel was still an idealist, since he gave prime importance to the mind, instead of recognizing, as Marx did, the primacy of matter. Since Marxism sets up such an opposition between metaphysics and dialectics, and refuses to recognize the mental or spiritual as a different category, it is necessarily atheist, if its idea of the world is to be scientific. But this is the result of falsely identifying all metaphysics with an anti-dialectic, static philosophy, of wrongly assimilating all spiritual philosophy to the radical idealism of Berkeley or the dualist idealism of Plato or Descartes. But what of the realist spiritual philosophy of Aristotle and St Thomas Aquinas? Such philosophy does not separate spirit and matter in any being at the phenomenological level, and although because of the then state of science it is a static philosophy, it nevertheless has in the idea of *analogy* a fruitful notion allowing the higher to be seen germinating, as it were, in the lower, while accounting for it within a spiritual metaphysics which can include the fact of evolution. To this, Marxism finds it difficult to reply, except by trying, in a way which is really not acceptable, to split it into a realist materialism concordant with science and a metaphysical interpretation belonging to an outmoded idealism. We shall see that it is precisely at this point that there lies the possibility of bringing together dialectics, in the Marxist sense, and metaphysics, in the Catholic sense, so as to deprive the Marxist of one of his chief and fundamental arguments for the opposition between science and religion.

Whatever may be said of this artificial opposition of dialectics to metaphysics, it still follows from the laws of dialectics that the Marxist must profess a materialism which, even if it is philosophically materialism, is nevertheless much closer to scientific realism, and therefore much more in accord with the religious view of the Christian, than the materialism of the old scientific rationalist.

THE EMERGENCE OF MIND

The Marxist holds that there is in the world only matter in evolution. This matter is extraordinarily complex even at the most elementary level of sub-atomic particles, where the problem of indeterminacy proves not the impossibility of the observer's understanding matter, nor the triumph of irrationality, but the simple fact that things do not always correspond to the false and simplified mechanistic ideas built up in the old anthropomorphic way. "Matter is inexhaustible," they say. Life and thought are only properties of matter; but this is a very highly complex and highly organized matter, and this complexity and organization give it new properties. The organic cannot be assimilated to the inorganic, nor man to animals, because the quantitatively increasing complexity of matter makes new qualities emerge.

In any living thing there are only atoms and molecules of the same kind as in the inorganic world, obeying the same physico-chemical laws. But now it is a matter of the special operation of these laws in a material environment which is complex and organized. In man there is nothing besides the living cells, but the presence of a brain made up of thousands of millions of neurons all interconnected makes him sufficiently integrated to permit the emergence of a higher mind. The psychological inferiority of a monkey is simply a consequence and a reflection of the less complicated nature of its brain.

Pavlov was the first to demonstrate the relations between the brain and thinking. He disproved the mechanistic hypotheses of those physiologists who tried to localize thoughts in particular neurons, as cerebral secretions, by showing that thought resulted from the working of the brain as a whole, and cannot be separated from that activity. And it was Pavlov, particularly, who insisted on the special features of human thinking. The primary system of symbolization, based on the reflection of the outside world in the brain through messages in the sensory nerves, is completed in man by the addition of a second system, language, the reflection of the world in words. This, being adapted to and making possible abstraction, is the peculiarly human mode of thought. The complexity of the brain which makes language possible surely gives rise to new qualities. Far from monkey and man having related brains differing only in their mental dimensions, so to speak, they have brains anatomically similar but physiologically very different, since man's brain has four times as many neurons as a monkey's, which infinitely increases the possible number of interconnections, the foundations of thinking.

During the past ten years, under the name of *cybernetics*, a fruitful comparison has been developed between automatic machines, sometimes called electronic brains, and the brain proper. Although these machines surpass the human brain in many respects, especially in the speed with which they calculate, they are nothing like as complicated. Some people have therefore thought that a great increase in the number of cells and their interconnections would make possible the emergence of consciousness. Such a suggestion shocks those who believe the mind to be spiritual; but neither does the Marxist accept it as agreeing with his idea that quantitative complexity produces qualitative differences. For the Marxist, as for a biologist, consciousness is a consequence of increased complexity, but of a special kind, of a living organism; it cannot emerge from a collection of inanimate elements however complex their inter-connections. It is obvious, then, that Marxism does not assimilate the organic to the inorganic, the superior to the inferior. In the process of increasing complexity there are jumps which bring into being true specific differences. Life is not simple matter animated from without by some spiritual principle, but complex and organized matter. Many examples could be given of the humanist consequences which should follow from this recognition by Marxism of the mind of man as a new property of the brain. As the organ of personality, ensuring the unity of the acting and thinking being, it should be respected. Already, in dealing with animals, Pavlov tried to study the normal working of the brain of a subject awake, attentive, and free of all experimental mutilation. In this he was showing the way, even so early, for modern neurophysiology. The subjects of the experiments were not interchangeable; each reacted in a way dependent on its individuality and its particular past. This is directly opposed to Descartes' idea of animals as machines.

Under the influence of this manner of thinking, to change the personality of a man, even of the insane, by neurological operations (lobotomy) is forbidden by law in the Soviet Union. Here we have a materialism with what seems like more respect for human personality than some spiritual philosophies: all human personality is bound up with the brain. The rejection of the mind-body dualism has fruitful consequences in the field of psycho-somatic phenomena, since it is no longer a question of the mysterious interaction of mind and body, but of the influence of the brain on the rest of the organism. Suggestion has a physiological explanation; the rôle of the central nervous system in pathology and in therapeutics becomes clear. It is no longer possible to treat a sick man as a veterinary surgeon does an animal, without taking into account all his mental and social background. So the transition is effected from Pavlov's studies of the conditioned disappearance of pain in an animal (by linking it with a reward) to the psychological method of painless childbirth, in which a woman learns a technique of using her brain, which is rendered unwilling to accept or recognize pain. This is a remarkable example of the application by Marxist humanism of a scientific discovery, and Pius XII recognized its great interest and its importance, while freeing it from all its materialist colouring. We might also mention the perfecting of sleep-therapy, in which everything down to the smallest detail is worked out for the perfect well-being of the patient (sent to sleep and woken up by selected pieces of music and so on). In every field the accent is placed on the conscious act, on explanation, on education. To the passivity of hypnosis and suggestion is opposed the truly human activity of understanding. The development of scientific knowledge is of the first importance. When, in 1935, the International Congress of Physiology was held in Moscow under Pavlov's presidency, *Pravda* celebrated the occasion with a front-page article entirely given up to science. Today, the skyscraper of Moscow University dominates the capital of the Soviet Union. These facts bear witness to the importance attached by Marxists to science. Their faith in science forces them to get rid of more and more of the remnants of the illusory mechanistic rationalism which their antagonism to spiritual philosophy tends to preserve in their thinking.

If Marxism has a better idea of man than the old mechanistic rationalism, it is still incomplete, and that especially in the realm of consciousness. Pavlov was right to assert that physiology should not be concerned with consciousness as such: it is not a thing, which can be found at this or that point in the brain. To explain an organic reaction in terms of some psychological entity is a kind of word-play which impedes the scientific study of cerebral mechanisms, which is the proper study of the neurophysiologist. So he must ignore or forget consciousness. Conscious or not, processes in the brain work in similar ways. So it becomes easy to consider consciousness, now cut out of the realm of cerebral phenomena, as an insignificant epiphenomenon. It is the same sort of process that led from the separate soul of Descartes to the man-machine of the eighteenth century.

The serious deficiency of Pavlov's approach lay in its only considering the physiology of the brain under its analytical aspect, studying the interactions of the various innate and conditioned reflexes, with its consequent neglect of that new thing which arises from the quantitative complexity resulting from their synthesis and integration. The integrative action of the brain produces this new thing, as the *Gestalt* psychologists recognized, but they saw it as opposed to elementary physiological processes, whereas it is really a matter of the way these elementary processes exist and function together, as a whole. For Pavlov, the appeal to consciousness meant the introduction into physiology of a metaphysical myth; and this has been the attitude of a number of physiologists, like Sherrington, who remained Cartesians, for whom neurophysiology could not explain the mystery of thought. True, Pavlov saw what went on in the brain as the reflection through the senses of the external world, but he did not recognize the importance of another reflection, that of the interior world of the body, which through the image of the body and its expression in the "I", in some way makes the individual present within his own brain and consciously master of it. The most recent advances in neurophysiology leave behind the sterile arguments between Pavlovians and anti-Pavlovians and tend to concentrate on a picture taking account of the integrative processes of the brain and the neurophysiology of consciousness. This cannot fail to have repercussions on the Marxist idea of man.

At present it is Soviet psychology which, having regained its independence after its long subjection to neurophysiology and sociology, opposes to western behaviourism a psychology of the conscious personality. It is not afraid of this older term, as are the rationalist and mechanistic psychologists, since it is not necessarily metaphysical but involves an essential aspect of humanity. While American schools of educational psychology see the child as a young plant growing passively under the influence of the interaction of heredity and the environment, Soviet materialist psychology insists on the third, more truly human factor, the progressive activity of the conscious personality, which makes the child gradually master of his own fate. True, this conscious personality is not yet seen whole, in all its aspects, probably because of the lack of sufficient neurophysiological knowledge. It is still seen as a simple reflection of society, as something imposed and brought into being from without, and not as the principal intrinsic character of the individual. Some spiritual philosophers, forgetting the Thomist maxim that there is nothing in the intellect which was not first in the senses, have obviously fallen into the scientific error of thinking that the child has a personality complete at birth which the development of the brain simply allows to express itself more and more, thus minimizing the importance of the environment, especially the social environment. The analogous error is often committed of overestimating the importance of heredity, over which we have no control, at the expense of that of the environment, which is in fact much greater and at least amenable to influence. There may be hereditary foundations for our personalities, in our actual constitution; but the changes brought about by the environment are very much more important for our character and our conscious lives, for they condition the greatest psychological differences now existing between classes and between races.

Cases of beast-children, entirely de-humanized by their growing up outside human society, and the inverse cases of savage children totally assimilated to our culture when they are transplanted before they are five, the age at which the brain begins to lose its adaptability, prove the importance of the environment. The mentality, the conscious life of a man depend above all on the cultural and linguistic environment. Man was fundamentally social from the beginning, needing for the development of his mental life emotional and intellectual intercommunication between individuals. So his psychological being is social and only makes progress parallel with the development of his society and culture. By means of that social culture, the consciousness of the individual emerged from the half-unconscious, collective mentality of primitive man—pre-logical but still human—and has emerged so far now that some forget that they are social beings at all. Marxism is therefore fully justified in insisting on the part played by society in the development of conscious activity: but this influence of society is only possible because man's brain is fitted and adapted for consciousness, this aptitude being the natural characteristic of man which makes indefinite individual and social progress possible for him at all. The social life of animals, even of apes, does not produce a culture, for want of sufficient brain.

Consciousness is an autonomous psychological reality, the dependence of which on the brain brings it about that it cannot be either developed or destroyed except by determining factors either in the organism or in society. But even if it is not possible to separate it from these determinations, it is distinct from them. A beast-child is still a man, endowed with a certain human consciousness which has not been able to develop normally. The depersonalization of consciousness in Marxism ends in the minimizing of man's freedom, which becomes merely the acknowledgement of necessity. Primitive man, said Engels, was no more free than the beasts. Only the progress of knowledge has set us free by revealing to us what has to be done. This is very largely true, for no one can be free without knowing what factors determine his actions, but this progressive conquest of freedom is the realization of a natural power of the human brain which enables the individual to rise above action in order to judge it. This power existed from the beginning and distinguished man from the beasts, but it was only a seed which society and education alone could develop.

Marxism is radically hostile to the nonsensical liberty of Gide and Sartre, the power to do anything at all: it is ranged with the spiritual philosophies in declaring that the only true freedom lies in adherence to a superior moral determinant. But in Marxism this adherence is not really true freedom: it is not the personal and free search for what is most human, but adherence to a sociological determinant which is humanizing so far as its end is concerned, but de-humanizing in its means. Human values, which are rightly removed from the other-worldly realm of idealism and set back in reality, then appear mutilated, since they are imposed on man from without by society, which need take no account of freedom. Society is re-formed, not men, who must obey, and subordinate their own ethics to the interests of social reform, with no regard for any particular ethical absolute. There is an ethical absolute: but it is only in the future—the establishment of the classless society. In the achievement of this end, all means are good. At present, all morality is relative and bound up with the class structure. In the classless society of the future all men will necessarily be good.

The whole Marxist attitude to the individual consciousness is thus ambiguous: the rôle of society is quite properly recognized, but the individual man himself is forgotten. This is a consequence of its mixture of mechanistic thinking, with its inability to recognize consciousness as a real function of the organism, and idealism, which makes it simply a superstructure added by society. There is no need for a spiritual philosophy to object to this; it can be done simply on the grounds of scientific realism. This is surely the fundamental problem of Marxism: here is the root cause of its deficiency as humanism and of its intolerant political totalitarianism. A real materialist who is also truly scientific cannot allow himself to underrate man's consciousness and freedom, and he must give them their true value without denying the importance of society; but he will, of course, fail to recognize the real, distinct reality of the human spirit, and its true greatness.

THE MEANING OF HISTORY

As a materialist theory, recognizing a hierarchy of values dependent on the degree of complexity and organization of matter, Marxism must above all concern itself with the historical origins and development of these values. According to the Marxist, the time factor not only makes room for chance differentiation, but gives us the key to the meaning of the world by showing us the direction of its development. Deriving his ideas from Hegel's dialectic, in which nothing is, but all is becoming, in a self-directed development, he finds scientific confirmation of them in Darwin's theory of biological evolution. Instead of making up fictitious analogies between biology and history, such as might justify the triumph of might over right, or a racial theory based on natural selection, he finds a fundamental analogy between biological and social evolution: the struggle between the classes is the equivalent of the struggle for survival between species.

Without worrying about whether the universe is such that there may be other men on other planets or not, the Marxist holds that there is on this earth, whatever the mechanics of it and whatever the part chance plays, a determined process of evolution of more and more complex forms, which has led to the appearance of man. Given the conditions of evolution, it must necessarily lead to man, who is, regarded objectively, the most complex of all organisms. It seems very unlikely that this is the result of purely random mutations. Evolution would be more understandable if one could postulate a reactivity of the organism to the environment allowing the inheritance of acquired characteristics; but science has not yet succeeded in showing that this does happen (Lysenko's attempts having met with no success). This would grant man a wider possibility of continuing evolution by improving on nature. In any case, this direction of evolution is a biological property of the physical world presupposing no metaphysical design or principle. At the start, man was simply an ordinary primate, very different from contemporary man. But as a social animal, he developed, through the communal work necessary to his survival, his mental life, his mind, by inventing language. By a progressive transformation, he gradually became less animal, more and more human. Society, like nature in evolution, was influenced by precise social and economic determinants producing evolutionary change in the relations between men. History is no

more entirely a matter of chance, depending on the moving
force of ideas or great men, than organic evolution. It is automatically orientated in the direction of increasing freedom, and
men are carried passively with this movement. Changes in
methods of production and the upward struggle of the
oppressed classes bring it about that the various types of
society are not arranged in a haphazard order, but correspond
to an automatic evolution from lower to higher forms. Primitive
classless society, with no divisions between man and man,
passed into a tribal structure, and from that, with the differentiation of classes within society, to the slave-states of antiquity;
these gave place to feudalism, and then, with the liberation of
the middle classes, capitalist society developed. The revolution
of the proletariat, the last of the exploited classes, must necessarily lead to the final stage in history, the new classless society
wherein no man is exploited by another. So all social structures
such as the State, or marriage, undergo an evolution conditioned
by economic factors, which also determine those superstructures
in the order of thought, philosophy and religion.

In Marxist analysis man becomes conscious of this evolutionary process and ought to accept and submit to it. All he can
do is speed it up by supporting whatever moves in the same
direction and is therefore by definition good. It therefore
naturally follows that whatever does not move in the same
direction as history has to be sacrificed; naturally today is
sacrificed for the "tomorrow which sings for joy". History must
be assisted in bringing the new man to birth. Knowledge is
only of importance as issuing in action, in *praxis*, political
involvement in the class struggle in the service of the temporary dictatorship of the proletariat: temporary, because when
economic conditions allow, the State will disappear altogether.
The middle-class state is objectively, scientifically wrong when
it oppresses one class in the service of another, that other class,
what is more, having been left behind by history. The revolutionary state can only set men free, since it works for the advent
of the new man: it is the duty of every individual mind to be
merely the mirror of its just decisions. The golden age is just

around the corner. So some Marxists imagine, who cannot conceive the personal nature of sin. Others, more realistic, envisage a continuation of history after all class-conflict has disappeared: the dialectic of contraries which makes progress possible will then take the form of criticism and self-criticism.

So we can see how the whole of Marxist policy, in its criticism of the wrongs of capitalist society and even in the excesses of Communism, is informed by a scientific analysis which constructs a code of behaviour from the ideas of a world in evolution and man in process of making himself. Despite the Christian's belief in the permanence of values and the four last things, he finds Marxism a way of thinking not wholly foreign to his own, less foreign than that rationalist relativism which denies all direction to evolution. But the Christian cannot put off the actual achievement of values until the future. And we shall see how even from the point of view of science, though it confirms this idea of the direction of history, it cannot be said that history creates anything: it merely makes possible the development of potentialities natural to man from the beginning. Consequently, any doctrine preventing the full development of man's conscious liberty cannot be moving in the true direction of history. By accepting the necessity to submit to an automatic movement of history, the Marxist consciousness must remain alienated and alienating.

ATHEIST METAPHYSICS

By definition, Marxism is an evolutionary philosophy of nature opposed to any metaphysics maintaining the idea of permanence or the primacy of essence over existence. Diametrically the opposite of rationalism, which concludes that the world is irrational, it reveals all the meaning of the world. If it contented itself with being a phenomenological interpretation aiming at influencing action, it would not naturally be opposed to religion: the facts asserted by Marxism do not in themselves contradict the faith. If, then, Marxism does derive from science an assured atheism, it is because it is not a purely scientific philosophy, but adds to its dialectics of nature a philosophical interpretation which is anti-religious. Despite the Marxist's opposition to all metaphysics, this interpretation is nonetheless metaphysical; but it is a negative metaphysics.

According to this metaphysics, the coherence of a world in which values appear by evolution because of the increasing complexity of material organisms, is a proof, and a sufficient proof, of its autonomy, and disproof of the need for a Creator God. The Marxist asserts that the emergence of mind is of secondary importance, because it is matter which brings it into being; but he refuses to analyse this idea of matter philo-sophically, matter which is given to us in sensible experience. By taking consciousness to be a function of the material brain, he denies the existence of a soul, and concludes that man is wholly mortal. From the fact that man is evolved from the same stock as apes and other primates, he deduces that man is an animal made human by communal, collective labour.

It then follows that God and spiritual values are simply inventions of primitive man in his ignorance: he needed to be reassured against his fears and anthropomorphized natural forces or social taboos. In later ages, the ruling classes had a vested interest in keeping up these beliefs in order to keep the working classes in submission by promising them an illusory paradise after death. Based on obedience and resignation, hallowing and projecting into the Beyond the dependence of the inferior on the superior, and declaring that authority is divine, religion is not only a mark of ignorance: it alienates man in preventing him from becoming aware of his duty with relation to history. It hinders progress by vainly hoping to put a stop to the class war, on which the movement of history depends. The very forms of theology are conditioned in each age by social conditions: the angelic hierarchy is an image of the feudal system. To fight against religion is not only to educate man, but to set him to work again at his proper task. In a Communist society, religion is forced to disappear as being the lingering reflection of a lost illusion. Communist man is as necessarily atheist as the classless society, since social and economic conditions suppress religion as a visible phenomenon. The Marxist thinks he can find the justification for his course of action in history. He will not see that to point to various deviations from religion in history, and the wrongdoings of religious men, is not to argue against the truth of religion itself at all.

PART II

THE SEPARATION OF SCIENCE AND RELIGION
(ATHEIST AGNOSTICISM AND CHRISTIAN FIDEISM)

CHAPTER IV

AGNOSTIC SCEPTICISM AND THE RELIGION OF FEELING

On the one hand, then, we have the certitude of the rationalist's atheism, and that of the Marxist, who derives his disproof of God's existence and of man's immortality from a slightly different but equally materialist interpretation of the scientific picture of the world. On the other, there is the faith of the Christian, a faith no scientific argument can destroy—he may even find confirmation of his faith in science—but that is not all there is: there is also the less convinced atheist, whose atheism is a sort of negative faith, a probability seemingly in better agreement with science, which he regards as materialist. He will readily agree that the old scientific rationalism and contemporary Marxism are really philosophical interpretations of a science in itself neutral. Science is neutral either because of its temporary shortcomings, or, more surely, because of its essential inability to pass beyond the study of phenomena, its proper sphere. Is there any other mode of knowing possible to the mind of man? He does not think so, and is unconvinced by the arguments of religious philosophers. The mind, taken up with the business of living, is surely incapable of knowing everything, and it is sheer dogmatism to think that it can attain to any certitude whatever on the question of the existence or non-existence of God. So we should be tolerant, though we should strongly oppose all forms of fanaticism. Science cannot destroy religion, because it is not its business to do so. If science never discovers God, Christians can always say that that is because God is not discoverable by science. In the face of the Church's assertion, and that of many Christian scientists, that science does not interfere with religion, and in the face of the arguments of Christians who, without misrepresenting scientific facts, find some confirmation of their beliefs in science, the agnostic remains unconverted, and clings to the atheist scepticism of a worried, or even an indifferent, "How do I know?"

If the agnostic is frowned on by the Church, it is for his atheism, for his refusal to commit himself, for his assertion that man has no other means of knowing anything other than the scientific: it is not because he maintains, quite rightly, that science cannot decide metaphysical questions. The Christian is perfectly clear that science is limited, that it is only one way of looking at reality, that it cannot totally comprehend the natures or essences of things. So he is a sort of agnostic on the scientific level, since he too asserts that it is not the part of science to concern itself with the field of religion. Scientific facts and theories are in themselves neutral but they are susceptible of either a religious or an atheist interpretation; scientific reasoning cannot decide between them. That is the philosopher's task, and on the philosophical level the Christian cannot be agnostic. It is by philosophical reasoning that arguments can be drawn from science for or against religion. It is true that it is most often the converted who are thus convinced, but still this must offer the possibility of the beginnings of grace. It is not that science and philosophy (or religion) are independent. They deal with the same reality, but from different points of view and with different methods and techniques. These points of view must be very carefully distinguished, to avoid confusion; but it would be as confusing to separate altogether the fields they cover. The mistake which is common to atheistic agnosticism and religious sentimentalism is to set against one another the realm of science, the rational study of reality, yielding certitude and useful, practical consequences, and that of philosophy and religion, where all is relative, unknowable, and of little relevance to action. Science is busy with the world: religion is merely the response to an obscure feeling, to the need to be protected against the pain of death. The agnostic, rational enough in his life as a scientist, who feels an emotional need for religion—a religion which really is an opiate—is very careful not to set before his mind two different views of the world, the scientific and the religious. He does not compare the two. Religion, for him, is not a form of knowing, but simply irrational. If this is so, omnipotent science does not destroy religion only because religion has been reduced to practically nothing. Science has become the only source of knowledge, of understanding, and of action; religion, cut off from its proper field, is no more than the personal satisfaction of a private need, which it is easy to call unreal and illusory. Whoever makes religion too spiritual, too divorced from the world, is very close to forgetting and losing the true faith. In any case, the omniscience of science, far from allowing faith to blossom, constitutes a very real danger.

Such was the attitude, as we know, of Pasteur:

> In each of us there are two men: the man of science, who starts with a blank sheet, and by observation and experiment and the use of his reason tries to rise to the understanding of nature; and the man of feeling, the man who weeps for the children he has lost, who cannot, alas! know whether he will see them again, but believes and hopes that he will; the man who does not want to die like a bacillus; the man who convinces himself that the force which is in him will be changed. The two realms are distinct, and woe to him who tries to make one encroach on the other, in this imperfect state of human knowledge.

Only a mistaken mind could try to introduce religion into science; more mistaken still is "the mind of one who tries to introduce science into religion". This last statement is ambiguous: it is true if it refers to techniques and points of view, false if it means the separation of the two realms as two realities. They must not be confused, it is true; but they must be brought together. But when Pasteur only asks religion for consolation, he is not far removed from atheist scepticism; indeed, that scepticism seems fundamentally more courageous in its stoicism.

In 1900, science seemed to be on the eve of explaining everything in simple terms; the world was rational, determinist, without mystery. God seemed to be cut out altogether, for the lack of philosophical thinking allowed Einstein's dictum to be forgotten: that the real mystery is that the world *is* rational, that man can understand it and base his actions on that understanding. More than fifty years later, looking at all that has happened in that half century, it is easy for us to laugh at that older generation, who thought they could understand it all. Where now is the simple physics of those days? What changes have there been in biology and physiology and psychology! We know now that there is still much that we do not know, but we have learned something certain: that the world is more complex than our over-simple theories, that we only understand and explain it very superficially. Established laws of nature and simple determinism have given place to the recognition of the statistical character of many scientific general truths, to the discovery of the strange and apparently indeterminist character of microphysics. The irrational has a foothold on science itself, and scientists are no longer sure that they can explain everything. May there not be something which is unknowable, not because of metaphysics, but because of our methods of observation, because of the very nature of our understanding? This sort of readmission of mystery, of the unknowable, has seemed to some to open the door to religion, as if God were there to fill the gaps in the scientific explanation, as if it were what is anomalous in nature, and not its harmony and order, which points to God the Creator. In fact, the problem is not one of metaphysics, but purely scientific. The irrationality of modern science has been too often overstressed and exaggerated. If men are worried by the technological advances which make possible the annihilation of mankind, and if they therefore demand some control of science, this is not because science has failed in any way, but because it has been so extraordinarily successful. If abstract mathematical calculations and formulas, which seem to us to give an idealist, abstracted view of matter, lie behind the development of atomic energy, we should not therefore be pessimistic about the future of scientific knowledge and its potentialities, despite the subjectivity of the brainwork lying behind it.

In truth, there is no reason why, within its own field of action, any limits should be set to science. Theoretically, there is no Unknowable in the material world, even if there may be a region of things practically unknowable which we cannot delineate. What are the limits of our technology, of our means of investigation? What is so complex that we *cannot* make it? If we would avoid the mockery which pursues those who try to fix limits to science, let us be careful not to make such general predictions, especially not to make them in the name of metaphysics at the scientific level. Insoluble problems only appear insoluble: the advance of science changes their appearance. It is even probable that when we do understand better, the very statement of the problem will have changed so much that the solutions once proposed will have ceased to make sense.

The material world open to scientific knowledge is infinite, and science must therefore always advance. Every day we learn more, and every day we realize that there is still more to learn. Man is a tiny animal on a little planet at an insignificant point in the infinite universe. He has astonishing powers of analysis and understanding and action, derived from his possession of such a nervous system and brain. But despite these powers, which originally simply served to assure his survival, how could he hope to be able to comprehend everything and judge, from without, as it were, a cosmos of which he is only a part?

J. Rostand, a biologist who cannot be accused of under-rating the potentialities of science, but who is rightly concerned about it, has reminded us that "when, after millions and millions of years, our species has spread over the whole earth, man will still be pondering on his own ignorance, still be complaining of his own lack of understanding. . . . True, it is the duty of the scientist not to set any bounds to his research—

but it is really just as reckless to say, *sciemus*, as to say, *ignorabimus*: there is nothing to show that all the secrets of nature, especially the most profound, can be expressed and translated into our local human dialect."

It is easy enough to see that each branch of science has its proper field of inquiry, that we do not use a microscope to look at the stars. It is much more difficult to make anyone see that there are questions with which science cannot deal at all, and that these are precisely those belonging to religion. Science is not restricted to collecting facts. It is not going beyond its proper duty when it seeks to order and group facts so as to achieve a synthesis presenting a scientific picture of the world (scientific cosmology), which must obviously always be incomplete and imperfect. But however successful such an attempt may be, it never attains to true philosophical and metaphysical knowledge. Such a scientific picture can tell us nothing of the essence of things, of the cause of their being; it can never include either the soul of man, as such, or God. These, we know, are problems which will always fall beyond the scope of science. Atheistic positivism concludes from this that they are therefore false problems, pseudo-problems, since science comprehends all reality and provides the only explanation. God is not an object of scientific inquiry, he does not come within the scope of science: therefore he does not exist, especially since he is useless as explanation, now that we have the scientific one.

The agnostic is more careful when faced with the same great problems. He is content to assert that they simply lie beyond the limits of human reason, and therefore should be left alone. The fideist sticks to the solutions given by his religion, but never asks any questions as to their validity; he is content to believe without thinking.

Is there, then, no other way of knowing open to man than the scientific, apart from the mystery of faith? This is what agnostic and atheist positivists maintain. In doing so, they seriously mutilate man's nature. Lecomte de Noüy professed a rationalist atheism for a long time, but was led back to the faith by his reflections on the scientific idea of the world. He rightly condemned those who put forward atheism as a scientific certainty, or asserted on scientific grounds the impossibility of religion.

Those who are honestly and sincerely unable to admit that there must be a transcendent organizing power should confine what they say to, "I don't know", and not try to influence others. Those who, without the slightest proof, have systematically tried to destroy the idea of God, are guilty of something base and anti-scientific. Far from being, as some scientists are (and I envy them), supported and helped by an unshakable belief in God, I began my life in that destructive scepticism which was then the fashion. It has taken me thirty years in the laboratory to be convinced that those who ought to have enlightened me—if only by admitting their own ignorance— were deliberately deceiving me. My present conviction is rational: I came to it by way of biology and physics. And I am certain that it is impossible for any scientist who really thinks not to end in the same conviction, unless he be blind or dishonest. But the way I came is too long and winding to be the best or the right way. And it is because I should like others to avoid the immense waste of time and effort that it cost me, that I now rise so violently against the wickedness of the bad shepherds.

The atheist agnostic ought to be completely honest in his agnosticism. He must recognize that science is not everything, that the limits and weaknesses of his own mind are not necessarily those of every man. Rostand very wisely draws a firm distinction between "the rash who believe that they know and the wise who know that they believe", and confesses, "even in my innermost self I am far from thinking that those who differ from me in their beliefs have not as sound a judgement as I".

Thinking, reasoning, experimenting; religion, philosophy, science: these three contribute each to the others, but none can replace the others. Even in the field of science, there is room for reasoning, and some of its probable truths are certain truths of religion. And religion is not simply blind faith: it includes the use of reason, and even some mystical experimentation.

A long time ago, Pascal opposed to the geometric spirit of science the mind's insight, the heart's intuitive knowledge, which gives us a comprehensive picture of reality, and which is perhaps more important to us than that derived from scientific analysis. In separating these two points of view Pascal was right; but Pascal himself set reason and faith too much at odds. It is at any rate certain that even if we should not underrate the importance of science, we should not on the other hand reduce the spirit of man to the scientific: neither goodness nor beauty is cut out by the truth. Philosophy has ways of analysing being which must not be undervalued; the aesthetic experience of poetry or music opens to us a world as real as that of science, and surely not unknown to the scientist. Reality is many-sided, and we have many ways of approaching it; contradictions between them are only reflections of the limitations of our own minds.

CHAPTER V

THE SEARCH FOR TRUE BALANCE: ORATORY AND LABORATORY

The unbalanced scientist has become so much a scientist that he utterly rejects religion as irrational and unscientific. The agnostic, while he recognizes that science cannot explain everything, will not allow that religion can know anything. For others, there is another field quite removed from the scope of omnipotent scientific thinking, that of feeling, the special concern of religion, which is wholly emotional and irrational. Though each of these positions is more or less acceptable to the scientist, the Christian can accept none of them, since all completely ignore the part of reason in religion.

Yet it is possible, in the same line of thinking as that agnosticism which limits the scope of science, for a scientific rationalism and a real religion which is not merely feeling to live together in the same mind without coming into contact with each other. It is enough to assert that the two are separate and then to balance the one against the other. There are no relations between religion and science; they cannot clash, since they are never concerned with the same problems, never deal with the same fields of reality. One deals with material, the other with spiritual, reality; one with, How? the other with, Why? This is practically the position of Pasteur again, but granting to religion its full scope and even its rationality. Theoretically, the powers of neither science nor religion are lessened, since each is entirely competent in its own field; in fact, limits are set to each, bounds that may not be overstepped. If the retreat of scientific rationalism has made room, for those who are not really Christian, for an agnosticism which allows a place to some sort of religious feeling, it seems that for a scientist who is a Christian, whether he is a theologian or not, the most generally accepted attitude is this one of distinguishing the two fields, of separating, in Grasset's expressive phrase, the oratory from the laboratory.

A man can be a true scientist without having to reckon with his religion, and at the same time he can be a true Christian without being troubled by his science. But does this apparent removal of all difficulties really show that there are no problems, that there are no relations between science and religion? Or does it rather show, with greater certitude, that the difficulties have only been removed by making a separation which is illusory and unjustifiable? There are not two realities, nor two bits of reality: there are only two aspects of reality, two techniques of inquiry. Each has not its separate field, but both are concerned with the whole of reality, of which each gives a different but complementary picture. To cut religion out completely from the field reserved to science is to deprive religion of an essential aspect; to refuse to develop science as far as possible for fear of encroaching on the realm of religion is harmful to science. Besides, such a separation, which aims at achieving a balance, is in fact deeply unbalanced and inhuman. We do not split our lives into two parts. Religion and science must necessarily come into contact with each other. If we do not bring them together in a harmonious relationship, they will clash, and either science will be dangerous for the religious life, or religion will lead to scientific interpretations of doubtful validity. The Christian scientist who wants to be a scientist and nothing else with his scientific colleagues, and a Christian with his brothers in the faith, will find that he is cut off from both, for he can no longer be either truly scientific or truly Christian. If we divide religion from science, they will divide us. It becomes difficult not to give in to a double temptation, that of scientific rationalism and that of fideism, reserving what is rational to science and what is irrational to religion. A fideist scientist could not be a true Catholic: he must ignore God as Creator of the material world, and know God only in some sort of personal relationship.

Yet we must not forget that to reach a true harmony of religion and science, which are different ways of approaching the same reality, we must get away from the confusion of the two. As a first approximation, it is right and proper to separate them. Science has, after all, nothing to do with God or dogma; it is an experimental and analytical mode of knowing quite different from the religious. On the other hand, the dogmas of religion are not current coin, so to speak, in science. If the scientist has no right to ask the theologian to change his doctrine in the cause of science, and this was the fatal mistake the Modernists made, the theologian has no right to interfere with scientific research or scientific theories. The scientist who is a Christian must beware of confusing the two completely: he should not, because he is a Christian, declare that living things disobey the laws of thermodynamics, or that they are only explicable in terms of some spiritual principle over and above their physical nature. The Christian neurophysiologist should have nothing to say, *quâ* scientist, about the soul or its immortality. There was a time before the development of modern science when religion fitted itself into a pre-scientific idea of the world, which it then found very difficult to give up because it had got to the stage of confusing that idea with the essential points of its faith. We must not do the same sort of thing again by transforming a scientific fact, which may be only of provisional validity, into a dogma: the expanding universe or Pithecanthropus. Religion cannot be entirely separated from the physical world, it must stick to reality: but it must keep its proper distance.

A scientific rationalism made to accord with religion would be as false as an atheist scientific rationalism. Totalitarianism, whether of science or religion, must be avoided; each must respect the autonomy of the other in its proper field. Religion's task is surely, so far as our means and revelation permit, to explain everything. It is to give the highest, ontological explanation, not to make up the scientific one. The task of science is to explain things at the level of phenomena, not to give a metaphysical explanation—nor to deny the possibility of such a metaphysical explanation. We should have been freed once for all from confusing the two by the struggle between Modernism and scientific rationalism. There is no such thing as a religion for scientists, as a small, separate sect: the scientist at home belongs to his own parish. Nor is there one science for Christians and another for atheists. In this sense, oratory and laboratory really are separate. We do not pray for a miracle to make our experiments succeed or to confirm our hypotheses. Religion sheds no light on scientific problems. Nor does it, as some rationalists maintain, take away our enthusiasm for research, for we do not confuse the two levels of explanation. Conversely, we do not prove the existence of God scientifically, nor do we discover the mystery of the Eucharist with our scientific apparatus: there, science can only see the unchanged "accidents", the bread and wine; religion alone discovers God in the sacrament.

It is comparatively easy, though not without risk, to establish a balance between religion and science based on the total separation of the two fields, when one practises a science having very few obvious connections with the spirit. The mathematician, or the physicist specializing in the study of inanimate matter, deals only with equations or experiments; *quâ* scientist, he is simply concerned with phenomena, with electrons and so on. Neither God nor spirit comes into it. Simply as a scientist, he need not wonder, What is man? He is involved in human problems only outside his own speciality. If he is a Christian, God is the mysterious person with whom his soul, the spiritual principle in himself, enters into some relationship. For him, there is the field of matter, which does not include God, and which is the object of his science; and the field of the spirit, in which God is found, the object of his religion. True, there is life, there is the brain. Yet how great is the temptation for the non-specialist, who finds in them material properties so unlike those of his inanimate world, to have recourse to a scientifically dualist explanation: life is matter animated by spirit, the brain a machine used by the soul. He is more likely to follow Descartes than St Thomas, and the latter's Aristotelian physics seems entirely at variance with his own science, if not mere playing with words.

An analogous separation is as easy for the psychologist and the specialist in the sciences of man; and often also, unfortunately, for the philosopher. They are all concerned with man's mind and its manifestations. For them, the mind is something different, owing its specific nature to the soul of man, and the body is simply matter used by the soul. The result is that their attention is drawn away from the mentality of animals and their social structures, and they tend to set man apart, so that the difficulties of religion are deceptively glossed over.

But it is much more difficult for the biologist to effect this separation, especially now. For a long time it was possible to think of biology as the science of the body, of that in man which is like the animal: cells, organs, endocrine glands, nerve reflexes, and so on. Emphasis on such an approach meant that the spiritual and mental life of man was ignored in what was clearly an improper way. Psycho-somatic relationships, the relations between the physical and the moral aspects of man, and those between the moral and the physical, were all viewed in a rigorously dualist fashion: as relations between an immaterial mind and a material body. This view is changing as neurophysiology advances. The specific difference between man and other animals is no longer purely spiritual, but has to do with the brain. We now know how man's brain, as the most complex of all, gives to man greater potentialities for thought and consciousness. This is a matter of scientific fact, which does not necessarily entail any particular metaphysics. But it is the philosopher's task to interpret these facts. Man's brain is not just one organ among many, but the centre of that integrative action which enables man to think and to control himself. When we consider the functions of the brain, we are making an objective and scientific approach to all man's mental life and powers. We can construct a neurophysiology of his freedom, normal or pathological, and we can end with some idea of the norm, an ethical system. So the biologist can no longer consider the mind as apart from matter. He is compelled to take up a philosophical position and to work out a harmony of his religion and his professional scientific research. The two cannot simply be left side by side. Either he will become an atheist materialist, though not a mechanistic one, or he must discover and understand how the apparent materialism of science is compatible with his belief in the spiritual nature of man. His position may be difficult and delicately poised, but it may still be the basis for complete unity in his thinking. At any rate he cannot avoid the problem.

For a long time, the advance of the frontiers of science has stirred up problems demanding a clear understanding of what really is *de fide*, what is part of religious dogma, what the Bible really means on the theological level. The question of the earth's revolution round the sun was one that was settled with comparative ease. Certain ideas in biology which in themselves, as scientific facts or theories, need not have called for any religious or theological censure, did stir up considerable difficulties. Such was the case with the theory of evolution. It seemed to get rid not only of God the Creator but also of absolute essences, since nothing *is*, it merely realizes itself gradually by evolving. This was especially so when evolution was extended, as it had to be, to include man, who simply became the end-product of one line of animal evolution. Such is also the case with neurophysiology, if it not only makes us no longer simply complicated bits of machinery, far removed from the spiritual, but becomes a neurophysiology of human consciousness. It seems impossible to set out the classic spiritual values and powers of man as before. What is the relation between the omniscient Adam of the Creation, before the Fall, and the primitive savage of science, scarce emerged from the brutes? Admittedly, Genesis is not a scientific account of cosmology; but are not the religious truths there enshrined themselves threatened by science? It is precisely in the course of his work as a biologist that the Catholic biologist runs up against these problems. If he is not a Modernist and respects the authority of dogma, he cannot live his Christianity if he feels that it is based on an outmoded myth. He must find, in one and the same field, some agreement between the two inseparable points of view, even if he knows that some mystery will always remain.

It would thus be altogether wrong to say, as seems to be possible from the expression "oratory and laboratory", as well as from the proper distinction of the two points of view, that there are and can be no difficulties, much less contradictions. These difficulties are spread abroad among scientists and Christians alike by the biologist, despite himself, because of his obligation to communicate his science. If the Christian biologist were not himself concerned with this question and did not suggest some outline of a solution, these arguments would become weapons in the armoury of materialist, and particularly Marxist, propaganda. Such propaganda cannot be answered by understating the problems concerned, but only by facing them fully and honestly. We cannot hide behind some dark patch of ignorance, which may drift away, nor accept the withdrawal of either science or religion. The Christian knows, of course, that no ultimate contradiction is possible, since science and religion both treat of the same created world. No scientific theory or fact can ultimately contradict any dogma, so long as the scientific theory is accorded its proper place and the exact meaning of the dogma is understood. Any contradiction must be accepted and then resolved, by distinguishing the two points of view, by understanding how one and the same world can appear to the eyes of science and religion in apparently, and only apparently, contradictory ways. Creative evolution must be reconciled with an evolutionary creation, which has a proper regard for God the Creator and his creation, neither ignoring essences and values in concentrating on their historical actualization, nor ignoring this historical aspect in simply asserting values and essences *a priori*, apart from the historical conditions of their actualization. The spiritual nature and immortality of man must be reconciled with the neurological conditions of man's mental life and its kinship with the varying degrees of development of animal mentality.

We are often tempted to find a sufficient answer in continuing to assert an illusory separation of the fields of religion and science, seeking places or moments at which the scientific explanation fails and needs to be made up by the introduction of a religious one. But this answer is untenable. Too much is granted to science if it is held that it can ever give a total and sufficient explanation with no theological reference. Religion is too much reduced if it is only needed to fill the gaps in science. Scientific and religious explanation are both concerned with the whole of the material world, but religion must take account of a higher level of explanation than is possible to science.

For example, before the theory (or the fact, as they put it) of evolution was more or less generally accepted by biologists, the theologians took care to safeguard at least the original creative act of God and the specific nature of man's soul. So we could have said, God started the whole thing off; then secondary causes came into play in an automatic way until the world was ready for life; at that point God created the first living things; then biological evolution took over, and life grew automatically more and more complicated down to the appearance of the primates. Since all these living things had only bodies, they were material: this process simply prepared the material conditions of the human body. When these conditions were prepared, God added to this body, from without, a human soul. On the same objective level, God, who created the soul, and Evolution (a goddess?), creating the body, are set side by side. God only acts at certain times when he needs to add something to matter. Materialists need then do no more than persistently declare that the world is eternal to show that it was not created; they have only to regard the soul as a property of the brain, man as a super-ape, to eliminate God's activity altogether.

Now such ideas as these are quite foreign to Catholic

theology, which can grant science its own autonomy without detracting from the activity of God at all. Evolution itself and its laws are the creative act, the way in which God creates from within, making all things dependent on him. Whether the world began or not, and on this question science cannot make any pronouncement, it is nonetheless always dependent on God as his creation, and everything happening in the world must be related to God, even if we find a scientific explanation of it. The origin of life results from the development of more and more complex forms of inanimate matter. We shall one day understand how this could have worked and reproduce it in the laboratory. But it is just the fact of this developing and increasing complexity which is interpreted from a religious point of view as creation. Why canonize Descartes and ignore the sound and realistic metaphysics of the Bible or the right teaching of St Thomas Aquinas? There are no animal-machines; there is no mind separate from the material body; animals, like ourselves, do not have a body and a mind, but they are body and mind together, animated bodies, an indissociable compound of mind and matter. The body and its brain are not simply matter but that compound, including the presence of mind: metaphysical analysis can distinguish them, but they cannot be separated. Biology presents man to us as very highly complex, right from the beginning; not an ape changed by communal labour into man, but a new species different in nature and more complex, capable of developing in society psychological potentialities which had always been there. This is not in any way opposed to the religious view of the mind of man as essentially different from that of the animal. Evolution, as evolutionary creation by God, brings all beings into being in their whole mental and physical reality, and man is only a special case because the special nature of his mind can establish a personal relationship with God.

Such an example can show us how, while respecting the two different points of view and avoiding any confusion between science and religion, it is possible to bring the two harmoniously together in one field, where their separation would make life difficult both for the scientist and for the Christian. Of course, it is often difficult to find a common language, common terms, and the reasonable caution of the Church is understandable, since she must keep intact the treasure of the deposit of faith.

The separation of oratory from laboratory could only be a temporary position taken up between a science reacting against a thoroughgoing scientific rationalism and a religion which risked becoming completely fleshless and divorced from the world. We know now that science must try to explain the world, and we must not underrate its powers of understanding or its scope. Because rationalist and Marxist ideas are excessive, even from a scientific viewpoint, we cannot conclude that science explains nothing or that it has nothing to say about the meaning of the world or the "phenomenon of man". Science is still developing, and it is developing more and more scientifically in this very field of man. The Christian, and particularly the Catholic Christian, no longer wants to seem to world, and we must not underrate its powers of understanding where Modernism went wrong. Now he must assert the full value of religious explanation, in which he sees a broadening and deepening of his scientific explanation. Oratory and laboratory are working on the same reality and are inseparable, but we must always be very careful not to let either deform the other: they only meet in their common object.

CHAPTER VI

LACK OF BALANCE BETWEEN SCIENCE AND RELIGION: PELAGIANISM AND MANICHEISM

As against either a thoroughgoing scientific rationalism which denies religion altogether, or agnosticism and fideism, which grant it at least some small corner to itself, it is possible, as we have seen, to construct a harmonious balance between science and religion. This is to be done, not by a false separation of the two realms, but by distinguishing the two points of view as each complementary to the other and operating at a different level. This distinction does not detract at all from either science or religion, religion being understood as Catholic Christianity, which balances so harmoniously the rôle of faith and that of reason in understanding and explaining doctrine. Such a balance, which is difficult to achieve, is opposed to the un-balanced views we are now going to examine. Those who hold either of these views imagine they are affirming what is more or less true religion, but both err in their theory either by granting too much to science or by falling into the contrary error of denying it any value at all. These views can sometimes be found among Christian scientists, but more often are implicit in the way some Christians, especially those holding strong political opinions, think of the relations between science and religion. Both views are fundamentally only particular cases of two great heresies which were once rampant in the Church, which was itself able to preserve the truth of both viewpoints in a harmonious synthesis. The two heresies are Pelagianism and Manicheism.

SCIENTIFIC RATIONALISM AND PELAGIANISM

Pelagius was the champion of the natural powers of man, who has no need of grace to be saved. According to his optimistic view, evil becomes a simple mistake, an error; and the whole tragedy of man—this creature called by God, redeemed by Christ, failing because of his carnal nature, turned astray by original sin, and subject to the devil's wiles—the tragedy disappears. This is a way of thinking in a Christian obviously related to that of scientific atheism or Marxism. Will not man's own efforts, thanks to his scientific knowledge, enable him to set up a "kingdom" on earth, a golden age freed from sin? Such scientific optimism, with its trust in man guided by science, is not necessarily atheist or agnostic. It does not necessarily lead to an immanent pantheism which reduces God to the soul of the world, or the God who is to come. It does not necessarily imply adherence to the faulty philosophies of rationalism or Marxism. It is possible for a true Christian, one fully convinced of the possibilities of explanation, action and behaviour given to mankind by science, one who has grasped the nature of God's creative act as allowing the working of secondary causes and as putting evolution freely into man's hands, one who has meditated on the willing involvement of God in his creation, which led him, since he would not violate our freedom, to death on the Cross—such a Christian could think of science as able to lead men in building the kingdom. Since science rediscovers the meaning and the principles of the world, it can correct the errors that spring from ignorance and sin; since it rediscovers the will of the Creator behind his work, it can have true redemptive power. We are no longer concerned with the Marxist's autonomic progress of history, which denies human freedom: now we are asked, instructed by science as to good and evil and what belongs to man, to put our freedom to the service of true human progress.

But are we not then led to count too much on our own powers, and so deny the necessity for the intervention of God in our lives, an intervention which may not always be spectacularly miraculous, but is still providential? To ignore the fact that the autonomy we quite rightly claim is really a responsible dependence on God, is to deny Providence, grace, prayer and the sacraments; it is completely to confuse the building of the earthly city and the city of God. However important the advice we may be able to ask of science, science itself has no power to command. It cannot make us do good, even if it shows us that that good is normal and rational, and natural to man, and that it is in the true interests of every individual and of society. What is compulsive is the mysterious acquiescence of our freedom; not a cold process of reasoning, but the loving adherence of all our being. If science shows us the great potentialities of man's development, it also shows us how great are the possibilities of going astray, how inhuman man can become. It is all very well showing a man what he ought to do for his own good: he will always have to decide for himself what is good and what is not, and he will do not what is good for him, but what he thinks is good for him, what he wants to do. In a world in which the conditions of freedom, so that it be true freedom and truly human, cannot be laid down, scientific optimism has no place. Evil will always exist, and to such a degree that it appears objective and scientific evidence for man's original sin if not for the devil. We Christians, then, while recognizing all that science has to offer in the field of human behaviour, must not presume too much on our own powers. We must not forget that we do need help, we need a Saviour and a Church, not so that we need do nothing ourselves except repeat, "Lord, Lord", but so that we may be able to act at all and to perceive the truth. Nor must we lose sight of the fact that it is not in the power of the atheist's denial to suppress the presence of the Providence of God among men: all men need God, and all receive his help, even if they are not aware of it. It is surely the great merit of Catholic Christianity that it has been able to affirm at one and the same time both the rôle and function of grace, and those of man's freedom, as two complementary aspects of the mysterious relation between man and his Creator. This affirmation of the freedom of man subject to grace, with which we are often reproached by Protestants, is one of the marks of that realism of Catholicism which makes it peculiarly adapted to the modern world of science and technology—which is just the opposite of what is so often said of Catholicism. It is a religion in which nature, even when deformed, preserves an essential goodness because of the very fact that it was created by God. It is thus a religion which can acknowledge the autonomy of natural ideas about the world and man—scientific, moral and political ideas and so on—as not needing to be ordered and guided by religion, but as finding in religion, simply because of a dependence which is recognized, their justification and their full achievement.

THE MANICHEE'S REJECTION OF SCIENCE

Such a Pelagian attribution of too much power to science, to human knowledge, is one of the two complementary positions of unbalance Christians are tempted to occupy. The other, no less dangerous to true religion, and so common among Christians that it is sometimes almost counter-apologetics, is that ancient Manichean pessimism which took over from Gnosticism, infected the Albigensian *Cathari* and the Jansenists, and had a great influence on Protestantism. This view recognizes the existence of evil, but disastrously over-simplifies in equating evil simply with the world, opposing the flesh, the body, matter, to spirit and God, to the Good. Not all have gone so far as to oppose to God a God of evil; but matter, far from being created such that its spiritual content is ever-increasing, is regarded as a fall, an exile, for the spirit. All that any man can do is await with resignation the end of his stay in this vale of tears, where only one thing is important, to save his own soul by despising the flesh and the material world, by mortifying himself to the world, by abjectly renouncing his self. All the so truly human and Christian meaning of suffering and self-denial, which are such positive means for the achieving of a true balance in the recognition of man's proper limitations, is thus distorted and lost. No position is more opposed to that truly scientific idea of the world which attaches prime importance to the Creation, and which shows us that man, in working for the establishment of a just society, is fulfilling the will of God and creating the conditions for our salvation. No conception has done more to encourage Marxists in speaking of the alienating effect of religion and of the utter ineffectiveness of such a religion of resignation.

Now such a view has never been held by the Church. It is strictly heretical. In this view, as in the other, there is a false division: not content with dissociating matter from spirit, it identifies matter and evil. Sometimes this can result in a split between two lives, a professional and materialist life aimed at personal gain, and a religious life utterly indifferent to responsibility and only concerned with a personal, spiritual perfection having nothing to do with the body. If there is indeed some evil which is only a consequence of the imperfection of the creature, the true measure of evil is sin; in neither case are we concerned with matter only but with the whole being, matter and spirit. The identification of St Paul's distinction between the flesh and the spirit with Descartes' between body and soul is a serious error against biblical metaphysics. When St Paul condemns the flesh, he is not speaking of our bodies, but of all our propensities towards evil. In the same way, the highly ambiguous word "world" in St Paul means both God's wonderful creation and the human world of sin. We here below cannot separate the wheat from the tares.

If we must reject scientific optimism, which denies the reality of evil, no less must we reject this radical pessimism. It leads to a complete separation of God from the world. It leads also to the misapprehension of the modern world of science and technology, to seeing it not as a mixture of obedience and sin, but as a Promethean, devilish revolt of the creature pursuing a dream of power opposed to the will of God, a revolt bound to bring terrible disaster in its train. God will punish us for trying to do without him.

Like the scientific atheist, the modern Manichee believes that science destroys religion, but this is because science is utterly and essentially wrong. So religion is bound to fight it. Nothing good can come of it. From the spiritual point of view, all scientific progress is destructive. The Christian's duty is to oppose it, the more so since it destroys faith and distorts religion by emptying it of its substance. To seek to improve man's condition, to abolish social classes, to alter property rights—this is to attack the laws of God, fixed from all eternity, which prescribe that every man shall keep his proper place. Scientific explanation is useless, for it is religion's task to explain: the gains of science are religion's losses. No distinction is drawn between atheist Marxism and the scientific view of the world: the latter seems to be materialist, since it is, after all, concerned with matter. The over-stressing of our inheritance, the denial of evolutionary change, the systematic opposition to all that science brings forward—such are the habits of thought of the modern Manichee, who thus fails completely to understand either science or religion. Of course, there are all sorts of intermediate positions between those who are wholly anti-scientific and anti-modern, and those who do not understand the meaning of science and so are afraid of it, those who underrate the potentialities of science in the cause of defending the rights of religion. But all are obviously interrelated.

PART III

THE RECONCILIATION OF SCIENCE AND RELIGION (SCIENCE AND APOLOGETICS)

CHAPTER VII

APOLOGETICS AND SCIENTIFIC "PROOFS" OF RELIGION

THE IMPORTANCE OF SCIENCE TO RELIGION

The Church has never, even in the heyday of scientific rationalism, desired to oppose science. She has always affirmed, through the popes and through her bishops, even those who might be thought most opposed to the errors of the modern world, her complete sympathy and respect for science's struggle to gain knowledge in order to improve man's condition. She has condemned, in the syllabus of 1864, those who think that "the decrees of the Apostolic See and of the Roman Congregations impede the free advance of science". She rejoiced to see, at the end of the nineteenth century, the coming together again of Catholic thought and science. Their first meeting had culminated in the Modernist controversy. She holds that it is today the duty of every Catholic to be fully men of their own time, and that it is the duty of Catholic scientists to be recognized as the equals of their non-Catholic colleagues as scientists and technologists. Science and the future of the world must not be left solely in the hands of the atheists: it would be better if scientific progress could be looked after by men who believe in religious and moral values. In the years of unhappy misunderstanding, which seemed to show her as opposed to science, the Church claims only to have defended essential religious truths when these have seemed to be under attack or threatened by scientists or materialists making too much of temporary difficulties or unresolved contradictions.

If anyone asserts in the name of Copernican cosmology that the Bible is wrong and that it can be interpreted as one likes, the Church is compelled to intervene at once to protect the truth of the Scriptures. But it needed years of further theological thinking to make clear what is unalterable, revealed truth in the Bible, and what is only the contemporary manner of expression of the writer. In the same way, if anyone denies, in the name of evolution, any absolute, any creation, any superiority of man, the Church cannot keep silent. It is because scientists, or popularizers of science, have stepped beyond the limits of science into the field of religion, that the Church has had to reply. And sometimes, answering before sufficiently deep consideration has taken place, she has seemed to make the mistake of taking up a particular scientific standpoint, forbidding in the name of religion this or that scientific opinion. Disturbed by the overturning of the ancient and habitual idea of the universe by a new notion, still a matter of dispute among astronomers themselves, theologians were not always realistic enough to distinguish what was legitimate scientific hypothesis from what was inadmissible metaphysical interpretation. When it is asserted that man descended from an ape and that God does not exist, or that man has no soul, it is tempting to argue that the scientific ideas which lead to such conclusions must be false, because God does exist, and so on. But really we should be content to say that it is only that the metaphysical deductions go beyond what is possible to science. We should not say, man is not descended from an ape, because God exists, but that it does not matter much whether he is or not. The scientists must decide that for themselves, freely; it has nothing to do with the existence or non-existence of God or the soul. Eventually scientists and theologians come to see eye to eye. But those who are not Catholics should not imagine that the Church first opposed science, and in the end had to withdraw and abandon her own position, changing her doctrine. That would be wrong: she has merely had to change her way of speaking.

It is, of course, extremely difficult to lay down a strict boundary between science and religion. It is not possible to replace Genesis completely by a scientific account made up with a theological commentary. On the one hand, science has not completely explained and never will completely explain the origin of man, which is a historical event out of the reach of science. Scientifically, it will always be possible to believe in monophyletism, the single origin of man out of one animal stock at one particular time and place. Such is the prevailing opinion now, but it can never be scientifically proved true. Science can never decide conclusively for one or the other, monogenism or polygenism (one Adam or a small original group). On the other hand, even if we know broadly what is religious truth in the Bible and what is form of expression, literary *genre*, as it were, we cannot separate the two exactly and minutely, we cannot always know where revealed dogma ends and outmoded expression begins. We must be very careful not to lose any part of the treasure of revelation.

The Church in her wisdom has told us that she cannot at present see how the dogma of original sin is reconcilable with the idea of a collective Adam. This does not mean it will never be reconcilable. And we have just seen that science will never be able to decide the question beyond doubt. There is no conflict here, and we should say that the private speculations of theologians, who carefully consider the possibility of reconciling the dogma with polygenism, have their value, since they enable us to see clearly that there are two separate fields, that of unalterable dogma and that of the historical and material conditions of its actualization. In the latter, the Church is neutral so long as she sees that the dogma is unaffected. If science could prove the collective origin of man we should necessarily believe that this left the dogma untouched; if the two were not reconcilable it could only be because there were not in fact several Adams. There is but one reality, and the twin lights of science and theology can never dissipate all mystery. The Church is ranged with science in affirming the powers of man's reason, against all kinds of fideism; but science does not exhaust reason's potentialities. On the other hand, to accept that the reason is useful if limited is not to sink into the idolatry of rationalism: the Church asserts that if the reason can attain to the knowledge of God's existence, still it cannot know everything and needs to rely on faith, which surpasses it without being contrary to it.

So, for the Church, if science and religion keep each to its proper place, its own viewpoint, its own level of explanation, they cannot come into conflict. But this then makes possible a kind of tolerant indifference on the basis of their reciprocal incompetence. The scientist as such is a sort of agnostic, accepting truths of religion only by faith, in the strict sense of that word with all the meaning that rational theology has given it; and the theologian is a sort of scientific "agnostic", listening but never taking part. Not that this in any way prevents a healthy balance being arrived at. Every Christian has the double duty of being well informed in both the scientific and religious fields. Reality is one, even if our means of investigating it are many. We must therefore try to reach a unified conception of the whole, while remembering that part of that unified conception comes from science and part from religion. So we ought to be tolerant of those who, for want of science or for some religious lack, cannot attain to that unified view, which seems to us so evident and certain. Theology can make no demands of science. It surely does not postulate any sort of vitalism or fundamentalist creationism, but neither can it impose the theory of evolution as of faith. Science, as we have said, is not concerned with doctrine, and the scientist need make no theology. But does it follow that from the point of view of religion science must be neutral or indifferent, agnostic by definition? Has any thoughtful scientist, starting from purely scientific arguments, any rational means of separating atheism and religion and deciding between them? If it is not nonsensical, scientifically speaking, to believe, are there any scientific reasons for believing? Is unbelief fundamentally incompatible with science? Can we base an apologetics on science? Are there any scientific proofs of religion—of the existence of God, for example, or of the immortality of the soul—such that we can say that anyone who denies their truth is mistaken, scientifically?

We have looked at those systems which destroy religion in the name of science, and at those which declare that the two are quite independent of one another. Now we must examine those which see in science not a position of hostility or indifference but of positive assistance, those which claim that science can support and uplift religion, if not actually give rise to it. What is the Church's attitude to this? It might appear to be ambiguous. She has declared that the realms of science and religion are separate, and required that each keep to its proper field. But on the other hand, she has never, in her apologetics, refused to use scientific arguments against atheist ideas and in support of the faith. The point is that for the Church the distinction must be made, but there is no real separation or complete independence. Science is an approach to the created world, the work of God. Surely the knowledge of the creation, even when it is the product of the work of atheist scientists, who certainly cannot do away with God altogether, must teach us something about the Creator? Surely scientific knowledge of man must tell us something about his spirit? Philosophy is an autonomous field of knowledge. But surely a philosopher must think and reason both about scientific and about theological reality, and so reach a position of concord such that the rational effort needed to reach that agreement is forgotten, and the two realities thus brought into accord seem to bring science to apply directly to matters of religion?

It is for philosophy to give the natural proofs for the existence of God and for the immortality of the soul. Fideism is wrong in denying the powers of reason, at least of reason enlightened by faith. The argument lies between philosophers who believe and those who do not. The scientist as such has nothing to do with it. But that philosophical argument cannot be maintained at the level of the highest metaphysics: it must take into account the scientific picture of the world. So science can bring new arguments into classic philosophical proofs, and even perhaps produce new proofs. For the scientist purely as such, this is a matter only of possibilities: God can only be a more or less probable hypothesis. So the non-Christian need not necessarily be convinced by scientific argument, but will need purely philosophical reasoning, making room for grace and faith. But the Christian who himself knows that God really is, although that conviction does not come to him from science, can yet find in the scientific arguments such confirmation of his beliefs that he may fairly speak, in a shorthand way, of scientific proofs of his faith. This is reasonable, and there is nothing to prevent a man being converted in this way, as was Lecomte de Noüy. But it must never be forgotten that the significance of apologetics based on science is very different for the Christian and for the non-Christian. For the latter, it suggests a way of looking at things, it makes room for faith, it opens up a line of inquiry; for the former, it brings new and certain truths to his notice, because he already *knows*, and it is a matter of confirmation only, not of discovery.

So the Church tells us that science can and should lead us towards God through his creation. She has never said that science could replace philosophy and theology in proving the truths of religion. For the Church, the non-Christian is not making a scientific mistake: he simply does not see to what the scientific picture of the world points, though he often suffers from a want of philosophy and from anti-religious prejudice.

But this careful respect for both the autonomy and the dependence of science is not always characteristic of Catholic philosophers and scientists. In their enthusiastic and missionary zeal they want to pass on to their non-Christian colleagues the love which enfolds them, the God whom they reach through his creation in their laboratory, which has properly become for them a true oratory. If the Christian faced by science is tempted by separatism and Manicheism, or by scientific Pelagianism, the temptation which is perhaps the most dangerous and even disastrous to the true apostolate is what may be called confusionism or concordism: the desire to prove spiritual truths from science alone. This must end in intolerance and in the falsification of science, twisted into the service of apologetics. Nothing is more dangerous than to rethink one's science in the cause of one's religion. The non-Christian whom one wishes to accuse of scientific ignorance is bound to denounce this abuse of science, and will no longer think of the Christian scientist as a true scientist deserving of confidence: he wears glasses that distort his vision. We shall see how difficult it is to escape this accusation, even when one does remain strictly scientific. The Christian is very content with this sort of science, and this "slanted" apologetics serves as the foundation for simple sermons which have no effect on the non-Christian except to irritate him. It is often difficult for the scientist who is a Christian to oppose these false scientific proofs of spiritual truths, since he then seems to be opposing God and religion. Yet it is nevertheless his duty to do so. Apologetics should not be based on a science adapted for Christians, on a philosophy which is religious and scientific, and highly debatable, but on the truly scientific view of the world common to Christians and non-Christians alike. If we can justifiably accuse Marxism or rationalism of distorting science and abusing it in the service of atheism, let us not commit the same mistake ourselves, a mistake by no means justified because the abuse and distortion serve the truth. That truth has no need of distortion in its defence. There are probable scientific arguments for believing, although they have their limitations, and there is no need to invent false ones.

CONFUSIONISM AND CONCORDISM

It is right that there should be, in a perfect harmony between science and religion, only one view of the world. But the two must be distinguished. It used to seem to be required by religion that the earth was stationary at the centre of the universe, that all things were created as they are, all at once, in the six days of Creation, that man was in the beginning in a state of perfection in an earthly paradise. Came science: and we had unhappily to distinguish what was of faith, and what was known as true by our natural powers. Let us not slip back into the same error. Even if certain scientific theories are definitively established—and who would like to prophesy their future?—let us not make a theology from them. It is perfectly fair to use for apologetic ends some scientific arguments which seem to support the idea of a beginning of the universe. The hypothesis of an expanding universe is in agreement with the classical idea of the creation of the world. But we do not know what will be the lot of that theory. It does seem that we can never know for certain whether the world had a beginning or not. Opposing theories are equally scientific. We must be careful not to prove creation by such and such a scientific theory, because if that theory is abandoned, it will be thought that creation has been disproved. But even a perpetually existing world could nonetheless have been created.

The metaphysician appears to deal with permanent and unchanging things, and so some have thought that he is bound to reject evolution, as proposed by science. But what he in fact rejects is the atheist idea of evolution, not the successive evolving into actuality of different powers and different creatures. He is only opposed to a theory of evolution which goes beyond the purely scientific level and pretends to be a complete explanation of a world in which nothing is permanent and absolute. It is therefore perfectly in order to show that biological evolution is not opposed in any way to the faith, unchanged and unchanging as the latter must be. But it is not right to go on to assert that evolution is demanded by theology, that it not only does not disprove the existence of God but actually proves that he is present in his creation. Because we believe in him, we may perhaps the more easily find him there. But in doing so we must remember that it is science and science alone which shows us creation as evolving—even if an evolving world does seem more in accordance with God's way of working. All forms of concordism are wrong. There was a time when the days of creation described in Genesis were taken to be the geological eras: we have left that error behind. The inspired writer of the Scriptures used the ideas of his own time; he did not foresee our scientific notions. The progress of science has freed us from the crudeness of mechanistic materialism, has restored to man all his natural greatness, has refused to separate mental life as a different product of matter from the brain, and has perceived the biological foundations of a morality natural to man. In doing all this, science is coming into greater and greater agreement with religion. This agreement will go on increasing, but it is still fundamentally true that we are never further from the purely spiritual than when we objectify all that is spiritual as properties of material things. It used to be illogical to be materialist or to deny the evident greatness of the human mind. But today, dialectical materialism recognizes the thinking mind, no longer as localizable in the brain as such, but as the result of its functioning as a whole. It is thus much more difficult to reply, because as the scientific explanation becomes more and more satisfactory, so we can no longer fill in the gaps in our understanding by appealing to a separate spiritual principle.

That all sides agree in recognizing man's greatness by no means implies agreement on the immortality of the soul. Scientific explanation is only concerned with what is spiritual under its incarnate aspects; it cannot know or deal with that which is the proper field of religion. It might almost be said that the scientist who merely wants to be scientific will naturally take the attitude of Rostand, refusing immortality to the soul in the name of the solidarity of the animal kingdom. For the biologist, differences of mental level are the consequences of differences in the complexity of the brain. It can certainly be granted that the biological differences exist and are important, and that this fits in with the idea of man as specifically distinct postulated by religion. But there can be no absolute proof from science of this specific distinctness. We cannot simply prove that the most complex brain implies an immortal soul. It is true that they do go together, but only philosophical reflection and analysis can lead to this conclusion; it is not experimentally or objectively verifiable.

There are other false concords we must watch out for, such as the unwarranted assimilation of the indeterminism of microphysics to man's free will. Let us increase the area of agreement between science and religion, but let us restrain our enthusiasm.

We must not forget that our extrapolations will not be accepted by those who do not share our faith. The harmony and rationality of the world imply that it was created so, but that harmony is recognized by many non-Christians, who explain it as due to natural selection, rejecting all metaphysics. It is possible to admit that phenomena seem to display the workings of some sort of purpose, and to seek the scientific causes of this, without having to accept any metaphysical interpretation. Nor should the emphasis placed on the harmony of the world obscure the fact that there is some mystery, some absurdity, some irrationality also in the world, in which some have seen the mark of God's hand.

The scientist rejects what is abnormal, whatever breaks the laws of nature. We do not yet, of course, know these laws sufficiently well; we do not know everything, and many mysterious facts will no doubt be explained quite naturally, but hoaxes and illusions will remain hoaxes and illusions. The Christian who asserts the omnipotence of God very often accepts the marvellous and the miraculous too easily. The Church has always been very careful in such matters: she admits miracles, but does not go out of her way to look for them. She always seeks advice from competent scientists and doctors. We should always look for the most simple, natural explanation, and remember that what above all makes something a miracle is that it is a sign of God, rather than that it is or is not marvellous or spectacular. There is more that is miraculous in certain spiritual effects of grace than in marvellous cures.

When a miraculous cure has been authenticated as a cure by the doctors, this does not imply that its working was so extraordinary that any honest doctor must be converted by it. It is remarkable that the "laws of miracle", especially at Lourdes, seem to show a deep respect for natural processes. New limbs are not grown: at most there is a speeding up of the healing of a wound, the resumption of some function before the anatomical cure is possible. The non-Christian can, to take the extreme position, simply invoke coincidence, without denying the facts;

and why should not God use coincidence? Sometimes appeal has been made to processes contrary to the normal laws of matter, to the creation of matter or its destruction. There God does seem to become in a way perceptible directly in his work. But we should reserve judgement on such ideas, while the facts are only doubtfully established. Before we interpret some phenomenon in an extraordinary way, we must be sure that it really does exist and that it cannot be explained more simply. God wanted to be hidden in his work, which is apparently self-regulating. Let us not make him a God who is in some way materially evident.

GOD AND THE IRRATIONAL

One of the classical arguments for the existence of God is that deriving from the order and harmony of the created world. Science, however, has so successfully described the universe as an elegant machine, self-sufficient and self-regulating, that that very order and harmony have become arguments for atheism. A rational universe is a universe explained, clearly understood, rationalist, in which there is no God. Such a mistake can never be sufficiently refuted. The result of the propagation of this error has been that apologetics has defended religion not by affirming it as the only true explanation of the rationality of the universe but by pointing out every gap in the scientific explanation, by stressing all that is irrational in the world. Thomism is sound religious rationalism; but Bergson reopened the door to spiritualistic philosophy by pointing out the failings of reason. His effect, and the quite proper reaction he stirred up, should not be underestimated. He was quite right to diminish reason's extravagantly claimed importance. When reason, now become all-embracing, ceased to be simply an instrument of knowing and claimed to be the whole of what was truly human in man, he made it possible to restore the balance. Unfortunately, for minds trained in scientific rationalism, he seemed to prove that God could only make himself known through all that is irrational, absurd and incomprehensible in the world. The moment science is no longer completely clear in its explanations, the moment it seems to be in retreat, God becomes in some way accessible again.

If the indeterminacy of microphysics has played some part in apologetics it is because the astounding power has been attributed to it of enabling the scientist to recover his faith. This is as astonishing an attitude as that which attributes the harmony of the world to matter and only what goes wrong to God. God is indeed mysterious, and infinitely surpasses our finite human reason—made, nevertheless, in his image—but "suprarational" would better describe him than "irrational" or "absurd". God is not simply a cure for our lack of understanding or our weaknesses. We have already seen in Manicheism the temptation to reject science as evil. What we have just described is a less obvious distortion: the world of matter, of physics and chemistry, is divided from God in a strange dualism having nothing to do with religion. Every time an oversimplified explanation of the world, based on a science which is still undeveloped and somewhat impetuous, is proved false, God is reintroduced through the supposed gap, which, of course, is very soon filled. For example, if living matter seems not to obey the physico-chemical laws of inanimate matter, it must be because a spiritual principle is introduced directly by God. An anxious watch is kept for all quarrels between scientists. If some scientists voice doubts about the mechanisms proposed by Lamarck or Darwin or geneticists to explain the facts of biological evolution, these spiritualistic philosophers rejoice: God and creation are saved. When shall we recover the sensible notion that, even though the world does include mysterious and irrational elements, all, rational and irrational, are parts of God's creation, and this or that scientific advance or setback has no metaphysical importance? We must be very careful not to fall into anthropomorphism, judging the God of the galaxies, the God of the infinitely small as well as the infinitely large, as if he were a man. Suppose there is something absurd for us in the very perfection of some living processes, need they be senseless and irrational also for their Creator, who knows and loves every blade of grass? Let us beware we do not try to usurp the place of God himself, to judge the meaning and worth of the flea, or of Koch's bacillus, in the harmony of the creation.

THE DISTORTION OF SCIENCE BY RELIGION

To think in one's mistaken enthusiasm that one has scientifically proved God's existence, or to bring in God to fill the gaps in science, are but insignificant errors beside that which we now have to examine. Are there Christian scientists who distort the scientific picture of the world in order to make it more suitable to proving their religion? Non-Christian, non-religious scientists tend, because of their materialism, to minimize anything in science that seems to favour a religious interpretation. They sin by omission. The opposite is more dangerous, for it distorts not only science but also the relations between science and religion.

Science is the study of matter, of material things and the material conditions of the life of the mind. So it is bound to be seen as a scientific materialism. But it is quite wrong to confuse this with metaphysical materialism. It is realist, phenomenological, dealing with sensible things and their transformations. A terrible confusion has grown up between matter as the object of science, which is the thing itself, studied through scientific experiment and observation, and matter as a philosophical principle: if the philosophy is materialist, matter will explain all reality; if it is religious, matter will join with spirit in accounting for everything. Science itself cannot recognize the metaphysical distinction between matter and spirit as inseparable parts of the whole. Science can only know the individual object, without wondering whether it is metaphysically single or twofold.

The objective materialism of science, looking at things from a material point of view, thus becomes, for the metaphysical materialist, the study of the whole of being: philosophy is nothing more than a bit of scientific cosmology, logic and epistemology. On the other hand, the spiritualistic philosopher loses sight of the fact that the matter of science is the whole compound thing, so that science only knows the whole being in part, and is limited to the study of the material mechanisms used by a separate mind or spirit. Every Christian is dualist in that he distinguishes spirit and matter. But this distinction should only be made at the metaphysical level, not taken to imply a real separation at the heart of any being. As the object of science, any being is one. If, instead of seeing matter and spirit as two aspects within the one being, the explanation of which should come from philosophy, we consider matter and spirit as two really distinct things acting upon one another—which is the Idealist error of Plato and Descartes—will not spirit itself, either in itself or through its point of insertion into matter, fall directly within the scope of science?

Such a spiritualistic philosophy could not come to terms with a fully objective science. It would have to limit the material object of science to simple mechanisms, attributing the complexity which is clearly observed to the actual presence in matter of a separate, spiritual principle. Life is not the integrated physico-chemical functioning of complex matter; it is the activation of matter by a vital force. The apparent purposiveness of the development of the embryo or of increasing complexity in evolution are not the result of complicated self-regulating processes, of the properties of matter, but of the working of a directive force acting on matter. God guides evolution either by direct intervention or by means of an immanent planning. Man's mind is an immaterial soul controlling the machine which is the brain. What if there is an obvious relationship between man's inventiveness in fashioning tools, and the unconscious inventiveness of living matter in producing organs? This is not because the inventiveness of the human brain is a specialization of that organic inventiveness which nevertheless transcends it; that is an idea derived from the apparent materialism of science that a spiritualistic philosophy must take into account. It is because the inventiveness of living matter is the result of the spiritual force which animates it, which is related to our soul.

Such vitalist ideas, which give a purely verbal explanation of the problems of the existence and the integration of living matter, are now less and less in evidence. They dealt in terms of an unobservable myth. Critics of such ideas have clearly separated out the "idea of direction" which the observer forms for himself in face of the facts of biology, which do seem to present him with harmony, integration and some sort of directiveness or purpose. Yet such Cartesian, Idealist dualism still colours Catholic thinking very deeply, whenever it is dealing with man as a being in which the soul is thought of as separate from the material body, which it acts upon at some particular point. Sound Thomist realism is too often neglected. It is thus possible to maintain that an objective and scientific study of spiritual values is impossible; by definition, the materialist must deny the spiritual, since he only recognizes the body, and must assimilate man to the animals. A facile apologetics can then, from the evidence for man's spiritual nature, reject materialism. A good many Catholic philosophers, even Thomists, reject any agreement between Christians and non-Christians on any aspects of natural morality. Instead of being accused of wanting scientific objectivity in rejecting the spiritual, materialists are almost encouraged to ignore it if they want to be consistent, since what is spiritual falls outside the scope of the science of matter. Since science cannot be stopped from advancing to complete knowledge of the spirit incarnate, such an attempt at apologetics is doomed to failure. More and more, there will be materialists who are convinced of the spiritual nature of man and of moral values, yet who are nonetheless materialist at the metaphysical level.

The desire for conclusive proof of the immortality of the soul, in a world which only trusts science, has led eventually to a new vitalism. This, far from separating spirit from matter, and asserting that science cannot deal with the spirit, makes every effort to reintroduce the spiritual into the field of scientific enquiry. It is not a matter of deducing from apparently materialist scientific ideas a purely spiritual aspect of being, but of grasping spirit itself, whole and entire, scientifically. In short, it is a kind of spiritualistic scientific rationalism, asking science not for arguments consistent with or favourable to religion, but for a demonstration of the immortality of the soul as practically a scientific fact. Now this is, it is true, an attitude having the merit of asking the most of science, as concerning the knowledge of the spiritual; its potentialities are not underrated, and it can certainly attack the problems of values from the standpoint of human biology. Such an attitude does not split man into a material body and a separate spiritual soul. Is it not the dreamed-of harmony, is it not the scientific confirmation of the truths of religion?

In fact, such a position, which awakens the enthusiasm of many Christians, is unacceptable. It goes well beyond the actual powers of science and completely distorts it by making it take account of things which do not come within its competence. Not only would a non-Christian remain unconvinced, he would even be led to underestimate the possibilities for the application of science to the mental and spiritual field, since this would be presented to him in a context no longer objectively scientific. The old ideas of vitalism are in fact taken up again. Life does not obey the laws of inanimate matter, but not because it is matter animated by a vital principle, but because it is a special sort of matter, because it has a specific *energy of life* having its own laws. The idea of evolution is rejected, and animal and man are opposed at the biological level. The study of the specific laws of life, and especially of human life, leads directly to the postulation of an immaterial and immortal principle of energy in man. The vitalists were wrong in separating spirit and matter, restricting science to the field of matter, in the metaphysical sense, and wishing in this way to add spiritual forces over and above scientific facts. The adherents of this later conception fall into the most complete confusion, since they do not sufficiently distinguish spirit and matter in the unity of the creature. No scientist could accept such a distortion of science, in order to introduce energies of a type different from those known to physics; no theologian ought to accept such a materialization, or "reification", of the soul, thus assimilated to a kind of energy, even if its spiritual aspect is still respected.

Yet perhaps we are after all close to the real solution, with this rejection of mechanism and of idealism, this recognition of the potentialities of science for the knowledge of man. It is enough to stop treating the soul as a biological entity or as physical energy, and to accept normal scientific ideas. Science today no longer confounds the inanimate and the living, but still has no more need for vital force than for energy of life. It is all a matter of organization, of the degree of complexity, of the integration, of matter, of the ordinary matter and energy of the whole universe. It all depends on the behaviour of matter. There is no need to oppose a true, spiritualistic, modern science to an outmoded materialism, no need to distort science to arrive at the truths of religion. There is no need to make a new science: we can rely on science as it is, and so get back to the position of St Thomas Aquinas. In assimilating Aristotle to the Catholic faith, he definitively decided the questions of the relations between spirit and matter.

CHAPTER VIII

THE APPROACH TO RELIGION THROUGH SCIENCE

MODERN APOLOGETICS

A modern scientific apologetic should be the witness of a Christian who gathers together "the witness of the universe", not confining himself to his private, personal relationship with God, but seeking to discover how this personal God is God the Creator, master and maker of all things. This witness must be based on scientific knowledge. There does exist a scientific picture of the world. It is now, and always will be, incomplete. It is often coloured by the philosophical attitude of the scientist, and generally by his materialism. But one thing we can today be sure of: that the scientific study of the material world, including living things and man, yields a coherent and consistent picture which has true explicative value. This the Christian must recognize. When, at the beginning of this book, we set out the ideas of rationalism and Marxism, we used especially scientific facts and theories more or less generally accepted by all scientists, what can be called a scientific cosmology which appears to be materialist, not because of its metaphysical implications, but because of the way it studies the material world. The mistake the materialists make is to deduce from it as if by necessity an anti-religious metaphysics, in doing which they often neglect certain aspects of reality, and especially of man. The universe appears to every scientist as a complex of matter and energy in evolution; on our planet it has gone through a self-regulating evolutionary process producing ever greater complexity and culminating in man; in man, the complexity of the brain explains scientifically the difference between man and the beasts and his mental superiority.

So we should seek not to oppose the whole of this material explanation, but to show how this apparently materialist account can be perfectly harmonized with the postulates of our religion. The two poles of a genuine apologetics should be to assert nothing on the scientific level which would not be acceptable to a materialist scientist, and to demand nothing on the theological level which would be contrary to revealed doctrine or which might be tainted with Modernism, that mistaken confusionism which has done so much to harm the relations between science and religion. In short, we need to show how it is possible to unite the scientific outlook professed by both rationalists and Marxists, with insignificant differences, and the religious outlook of traditional, dogmatic Catholicism. The secret and hidden, yet nonetheless evident presence of our God must be seen in the very warp and weft of that apparently materialist picture. The man who does not know God can still, despite the evidence, fail to perceive him; one who has seen him can no longer be anything but certain.

The first duty of an apologist dealing with science is therefore to explain and to reassure. Neither science nor religion should be changed. The scientist who is not a Christian must know that he would not have to give up anything of his science if ever he were converted. He has to learn exactly what the faith does really imply, which is very different from what he thought it did. The Christian must realize that his faith and his theology are in no way threatened if he accepts the apparent materialism of science. He in his turn has to learn what science really implies and what science and religion really are. The existence of God cannot be proved like a theorem; but by being careful to reach a better understanding of each other's position, each becomes more tolerant. The non-Christian scientist has to recognize that the Christian can share his idea of the universe, while completing it with a rational, metaphysical interpretation of a different order, the possibility of which cannot be denied even if it is not accepted as true. He has to learn to distinguish what are scientific ideas from what is metaphysical interpretation, and to recognize both the necessity for philosophical reasoning and its value for the knowledge of true reality. The Christian, for his part, has to understand that a true faith which is divorced from physical reality is incomplete, and that the scientific idea of the world, far from being dangerous, is necessary if his faith is to develop to the full. He should no longer taunt the non-Christian with being mistaken. He should seek to show him that he grasps only a part of reality. He should no longer set up God against him, but reveal God at the very heart of his unbelief. The object is not to convert him, but to enable him freely to make up the deficiencies in his own outlook. When misunderstandings are removed, the way is made easier for the mysterious working of God's grace, secretly acting upon our freedom.

To be an apostle, to make an apologetic, there is no need to desire explicitly to do so. By the very fact that he exists, and that his thought is a single whole in which science and religion cannot be separated and yet are not confused, by his total adhesion to the two worlds of science and the Church, the Christian who is a scientist and who has no more problems—not because he has suppressed them but because he has resolved them, or at least envisaged the principles of their solution—is a living proof that not only does science not destroy religion, but it makes room for it and even supports it. The better scientist he is, the better Catholic he will be, without Modernism, and the better witness to the faith.

THE IMMANENCE OF THE TRANSCENDENT

It is not necessary to enter into all the details of scientific facts and theories in order to establish their agreement with the faith. What does demand explanation is agreement between the apparent materialism and evolutionary dialectic of science, which insists on the independence of all natural processes, with a metaphysics centred on what is spiritual, on fixed and separate natural values, and on the dependence of all that is created.

Science studies secondary causes. Scientific explanation, while it is sufficient for a certain degree of explanation making action possible, not only does not rule out another level of explanation which makes sense of the first, but actually demands it. We do not need God to fill out the scientific explanation: it was St Thomas who said that everything in the world happened as if God did not exist. But God is the supreme explanation which makes possible and which even accounts for the possibility of scientific explanation. It is the fact that everything can be explained or is possibly explicable, within certain limits, which implies God, not the reverse. The Christian does not simply need God in order to be able to explain: he knows God exists.

The Christian thus sees in any scientific fact or theory the way in which God acts in the world. Evolution is creative because it is creation in evolution. What is creative is a material process, which it is science's task to explain on its own level; but the process is only creative because the world is created. The independence of the process of increasing complexification is a real independence, but it indicates a hidden and secret dependence. The interplay of natural forces is the way in which the metaphysical truth actualizes itself in physical nature. The truth is not, "Everything happens on its own, therefore God does not exist", but, "Everything happens on its own, and this fact and its material explanation are so marvellous that the false mystery disappears and the true mystery is seen, so that it demands the presence of God—not the false God, the craftsman or architect who fashions the world with his hands, but the true God, Spirit, who cannot act like a man".

The key to all the difficulties arising between the apparent materialism of science and religion is to be found in a sound understanding of the relations between spirit and matter, the soul and the body, God and the world. There is no real religion without a personal and loving God entering into some relationship with man. Such a spiritual God is transcendent, infinitely surpassing the realities of the physical universe into which men are born. But he is commonly placed somewhere above or outside of the universe, on which he acts as it were from outside. This is a false idea. God is not anywhere else. He is everywhere, at the heart of all things, while surpassing all things. God makes things act, he secretly animates things from within. The pantheists were wrong to make the transcendent God fade into the non-existent soul of the world. But they were wrong not in affirming God's immanence, but in denying his transcendence. God is not simply and entirely transcendent: that would be a magic idol, not the true God. God is transcendent *and* immanent; that is, he acts on his own work only from within. That work, the universe, is as it were a thought of God. Its created state implies the constant immanent presence of the Creator, not simply some initial *fiat*. All that science describes, this self-regulating interplay of natural forces, is metaphysically explained by the presence of God and its dependence on him. Yet the world is not God. He infinitely surpasses the world.

The self-consistency which science gives to the world supports the materialist if the world is opposed to God as one thing to another. If, on the contrary, it is thought of as the cohesion produced by the immanent working of the transcendent God, that self-consistency is plainly in accord with religion. Of course, the existence of God is not thus scientifically proved to the non-believer. But he is prevented from making for himself a false image of God as opposed to science, an image easy to destroy. The non-believer should not then be surprised if agnostic or even atheist science becomes to some extent theological, as the relations between God and the world, since not believing in God cannot alter the fact of creation. The Christian can pass from immanence to transcendence, and know that it is the true God who so reveals himself. The non-believer, seeing merely on the level of immanence, goes no further than a sort of vague pantheism which grants God no true reality. If science, then, cannot prove that God exists, it is because it cannot get beyond his immanence. Its arguments must always be ambiguous: they can never convince the non-believer of the true nature of God, yet they lead the Christian to the very centre of his being, to the God who is present in his heart by his immanence, yet has a direct relationship with him because of his transcendence and the relative transcendence of the human soul.

This immanence of the transcendent God, who is neither altogether separate from nor altogether one with his work, gives us the key to all the relations between the spiritual and the material at our own level. The human soul is immanent in the matter which it transcends. It is not one with a material body; it does not animate an inert body; it constitutes that body in its essence, as its integrating principle, unifying a perpetually changing dust of atoms and molecules. When the material conditions allowing of the life of that compound of soul and body no longer obtain, there is no longer a compound, no longer a body, only the decomposing corpse. So far as scientific analysis is concerned, there is therefore not just a body separate and distinct from the soul, but an indissociable unity, an animated body, the union of soul and body. Only the metaphysician can distinguish the two: there must be no confusion between the "body" of the catechism, metaphysically opposed to the soul as pure matter, and the "body" of biology, which is the whole being itself, looked at under its bodily aspect, including the cerebral aspect of its mental life.

The biologist, therefore, cannot distinguish the soul or have access to it in its specific nature. He can only know the organism as it is, unified and integrated; not a principle or force or energy of integration, but the material fact of integration and organization. It is a material fact because it is structure and function of matter, but it is almost an immaterial material fact, because an organization persisting in changing matter is simply a manner of existence of that matter. The soul is not localized in the body, and has no particular organ, not even the brain; it betokens the fact that the individual man is not a mass of independent cells but an organized unity, which results from the embryological origin of the cells and various integrating mechanisms involving hormones and the nervous system. It is the philosopher's job to discover the soul in the fact of integration, and to distinguish it from the particles it integrates, without separating it. He must explain how the true nature of man's mental life, studied by the psychologist in its specifically human aspect and by the neurophysiologist in its inseparable cerebral aspect, leads to the postulating of its metaphysical characteristics. The biologist thus has nothing to say about the immortality of the soul of man. But, since that soul once incarnate (whatever its other possible states of being, such as after death or in glory, which science cannot know of at all, yet cannot call impossible) is only shown forth in the properties of an organism with a mental life, the biologist cannot in any way object to or disprove the existence of the soul or its immortality. He can simply say that man, organically regarded, is naturally endowed with a higher mental life than animals, and that this argues an essential difference, which alters nothing fundamentally if it is only due to increased complexity at the level of organic mechanisms. But the transcendence of man's soul is already evident at the organic level, in the phenomenon of *emergence*, the fact that the human brain is capable of taking charge, and of reflective thinking, which sets the subject above his own actions, which he can then judge. This is the basis of his freedom, and that freedom itself is immanent in the determinist processes of biology, but is transcendent in that it is the power to control those processes. It is not a disembodied metaphysical principle but a power of the brain, the biological emergence of which is an argument for its true metaphysical transcendence, which science cannot judge.

The neurophysiological study of man's consciousness, as a physical fact, and the biological approach to all man's powers, may explain their biological mechanisms, but, far from dissipating all mystery, set the mystery of man clearly before us and lead to that metaphysical explanation which fulfils all biological explanation. At death, consciousness in its physical, neurological aspect disappears. If that consciousness depended on a spiritual principle—which science cannot disprove or deny —its survival in another state of being is very likely. There can be doubts only about the ambiguity of the expression, "resurrection of the body", which must refer to a state of being not precisely comparable to our present life and body, except by analogy, one not obeying the physical laws of matter and energy.

If human biology tells us not about a material body, but about the organic aspect of human beings—that is, the whole being, under a partial aspect looked at from the material point of view—it is easy to understand that it is indeed human nature that is defined at the biological level by its individual differences. Human biology can work out precisely what is normal and so define what are pathological disturbances in the field of behaviour as well as that of the physical organs. Biology and metaphysics are in agreement against certain relativist philosophers who deny the existence of a common human nature, or the distinction between normal and pathological. The possibility of biology dealing with mental and moral powers and values from its own standpoint is not an unwarranted extension of its competence, but simply the result of its study of human beings as human beings under their biological aspect. Science must not be denied what is possible for it in this field, and materialists must be persuaded that when a Christian biologist gets the most out of his science in this way he is not giving in to a temptation to stray into metaphysics, but is still being objective and scientific. There can thus be, in this field, agreement between Christians and non-Christians on values common to both which are justified by the natural balance and laws of the brain, the physical aspect of the soul. All that is required is that such values are not simply and wrongly reduced to that level only, that it remains possible to explain them metaphysically.

This doctrine of the unity of spirit and matter in man, which agrees with Thomist philosophy's hylomorphism, can be applied to animals. The biologist tells us that they have smaller brains, that they are less highly organized than man; this implies a biological difference in nature, which comparative psychology supports. The Thomist would say that this depends on a spiritual difference: there is a true soul in man, and a soul incapable of true existence of its own in animals. The second idea is the metaphysical interpretation of the first. Modern science and Thomist philosophy have the same analogical notion of the similarities and the difference of organization. The Marxist idea of the appearance of new qualities by things getting materially and quantitatively more complex is one which can only be explained by such a metaphysical interpretation as the Thomist idea of analogy between increasingly higher forms. This analogy also works below the level of life, where the organization of inanimate matter also expresses the working of some force or power. This is very like Teilhard de Chardin's idea of "the within of things", even inanimate things. It is the scientific statement of the fact of organization, measured by modern science in terms of the quantity of information handled and organized; it is a factor of ordered energy, and so the inverse of entropy, the measure of disorder. It is metaphysically explained by Thomism. It is not a matter of obscuring the differences between living and non-living, of identifying the two, but of constructing a unified picture of matter with its different levels of organization. This fits in very well with modern physics, which no longer studies phenomena but the behaviour and transformations of elementary particles of matter and energy. The relation between the materialist picture of increasing complexity produced by the interplay of material forces, and the metaphysical picture of the hierarchy of forms whereby the immanent spirit becomes, in the unity of being, more and more transcendent, though they are pictures of very different origins, seems to suggest that the spiritualistic explanation has much to recommend it.

THE MEANING OF EVOLUTION

Confusion has arisen between two notions of evolution. That of Heraclitus and Hegel, who denied all fixed value, all essence, for whom nothing is and all is becoming, has been confused with the scientific idea of evolution. Marxism acquires a good deal of its ambiguity from this confusion. The first view, relativist evolutionism, must be rejected. Scientific evolution, cosmological or biological, in no way rejects values or the natures which evolution in fact brings into being. It is an error to assert that one day a monkey was transformed into a man. In the strict sense, transformism does not exist. Whatever its origin, a species does not exist until it is distinct from another. Man is only biologically man because of his brain, and creatures like Pithecanthropus and Sinanthropus had not yet a wholly human brain: they were not yet true men, but pre-human. In practice, man in the beginning seemed very close to the animals, because he had not yet learned to use his brain to create human culture. He had no true, developed language, but only a simple possibility of articulation which was to allow one to develop, which indeed made it a possibility even then, had social communication existed. We do not know where man began, but it is certain that he had a beginning. Biologically, there are no transitions, even if there are intermediate species. The idea of mutations, which is not a metaphysical dogma, fits in extremely well with the metaphysical idea of separate essences. The theory of biological evolution merely gives us the idea that biological species did not all appear simultaneously, but derive one from another by transformations—not progressive changes, but the replacement of one type by another because of a sudden change in the protoplastic structures of the germ cell.[1] The progressive hierarchy of forms in nature which St Thomas described as a sort of "still photograph", has a chronological dimension, a history; it is a film, not a photograph. But the time factor does not alter the metaphysical interpretation of a world in which values and spirituality develop and increase.

This also applies to ontogenesis, the progressive embryological development of each individual. Each is established with its own proper nature in the fertilized egg; so this single

[1] The higher is thus only apparently contained in germ in the lower: there is no development of one germ cell, but the successive appearance of more complicated natures, brought into being by a process of increasing complexification.

human cell is already man, that man, the given individual, with all his particular potentialities. The chemical properties of the protoplasm which make of the egg a man, an individual, this individual human living matter, imply metaphysically the presence of the soul, which we must be careful not to identify with the mind or the brain. Development is going to produce the mental organ, the brain, which will give the soul its mental and spiritual possibilities at the organic level. But the individual is very easily influenced in his development, and the hereditary possibilities can be variously actualized according to the conditions of the environment. Biology enables us to some extent to distinguish normal human development and pathological, un-human development. The embryo first, and then the infant, do not become man by changing completely and progressively; from the beginning it has been the man, potentially, and it is only actualizing to a greater or less degree its potentialities, its nature.

The fact that the environment can completely modify the development of a man does not show that there is no individual human nature bound up with the genetic constitution, but that that nature is actualized in an environment which provides the conditions for its actualization. One and the same nature might, then, develop in several very different ways. From the analysis of the adult it is impossible to say what is due to heredity and what to the environment. When the environment is seriously defective we can talk even of a true denaturation, of the impossibility of the individual realizing his own nature. Far from being opposed to the metaphysical ideas of nature and essence, biology explains to us, with its historical aspect, the conditions of their actualization, and also tells us what are the normal, or normative, conditions of that actualization. Science seems to say, man *is* not, he comes to be through the conditions of the environment. But this is only appearance: man *is* from the start, but he is only potentialities, which are or are not actualized according to the environment. The possible dehumanizing influence of the environment thus has a metaphysical importance which cannot be overstressed. It is true that the fate of the immortal soul is not changed thereby. But that soul may not be able to accomplish normally its incarnate development.

The historical and evolutive aspect of this actualization of essences is to be found also in the general history of mankind. What truth there is in what Marxists say about the meaning of history and the rôle of economic and social factors in producing a synthesis, a false synthesis which estranges man and his freedom, which the synthesis is intended to promote, that truth has to be taken up in an entirely different context. That is, the context of specific and individual human nature demanding actualization in history, of the ascent of the individual's consciousness and freedom, which is not the reflection of society's but an essential attribute of every human being which society should help him to acquire, not deprive him of. Such a spiritualistic philosophy of the meaning and direction of history is a philosophy of freedom, not making the individual the slave of society, but reconciling the individual and society by showing that the realm of intelligent life is one of a society made up of persons, not a society swallowing them all into its all-embracing self. Because he does not understand the true meaning of evolution and the biological idea of human nature, the Marxist has come to deify history and its determinism. So he has often turned in the opposite direction from history, which sets men free. He must be turned round to face the right way again. Christian evolutionism could help. It would be worth while contemplating long and deeply the similarities and differences between the Marxist utopia of an atheist classless society and the idea of a realm of intelligent life, the noösphere, also classless, but fitted to human nature as well as to the divine will. This last does not imply that it will come to be automatically; its mystical prototype is the communion of the saints, that other classless society.

THE AMBIGUITY OF THE WORLD

There is no parallel between the division of men into those who believe and those who do not, and that into optimists and pessimists. Among Christians, there are some who see the world as ending in apocalyptic horrors, followed by the re-creation by God of the heavenly Jerusalem. Others think that man will come to wisdom little by little, and that God will merely have to set the seal on those who build the perfect society. Among atheists, some, as we have said, believe the world to be fundamentally meaningless, while others, like the Marxists, claim that history has a direction, leading us automatically, through whatever nameless horrors, to a true golden age. Apologetics need not, therefore, take sides in this debate. But if it is to be realistic it should show that the world is indeed ambiguous, and that we cannot possibly know the future, even if history has a meaning. A scientific apologetics should not merely use arguments relating to the harmony of the world: it should also use arguments pertaining to the world's antagonisms and to Christian pessimism.

We have seen that there are, despite a fundamental and radical opposition, elements common both to the Marxists' idea of the direction of history and to Christian eschatology. The idea that we have a task to accomplish, the making of ourselves and of humanity—not anyhow but in conformity with our nature, which is actualized automatically provided the environment is not too hostile and provided we want it to be—this is a profound idea, scientifically and metaphysically regarded, in which lies the distant possibility of agreement between Christians and Marxists, when the latter have recognized all the moral implications of the psycho-biological nature of man. We are talking of what man ought to do, what he can do if he acts in conformity with the direction of history, which is to say, in conformity with the will of God. There is always a certain in-built tendency towards this happy eventuality, for this world is a created world, guided in an immanent way by love. But man, the flower of evolution, is a creature fitted to be free, who sets himself free by his knowledge; so he is the one to take in hand the furthering of evolution. Man can and should further it in the right direction, towards greater humanity. But he has the power to wreck everything, for he himself can decide be-tween good and evil, and can refuse advice, biological and theological, in the moral order. We can insist on what ought to happen, on what is normal, without being utopian or denying the pathological possibilities of the misuse of freedom.

Of course, all is not for the best in the best of all possible worlds. Nor will it ever be. Those rationalists who point out the absurdities of the world are not wrong. Christianity does not demand such an unrealistic attitude. The possibility of success presents us with a remarkable agreement between science and religion. As much agreement is justified by the probability that we shall be foiled, despite all our efforts. Will humanity disappear in a cataclysmic atomic explosion, or by frittering away its resources for want of sensible control, or in a totalitarianism which utterly destroys liberty? All are possible; but so is a harmonious community of intelligent beings. This is the norm: the others are deviations from the norm because of ignorance or sin. But the likelihood is that evolution will go on its ambiguous way, with a mixture of good and evil. As ignorance decreases, more and more men will be enabled to understand their duty better, to discover what actions are at the same time productive of cerebral equilibrium, social equili-brium, conformity with man's vocation, and conformity with the will of God. But as man progresses and pathological, deter-minist deviations are removed, so he will be ever more free, and thus more free to sin, more responsible. Goodness is not, and never will be, automatic. The harmony of creation must not obscure the fact that we live in an absurd world, as many scientific observations confirm. These are in striking agreement with Christian ideas: the world is imperfect, for it is not God; it is unfinished, for it is evolving; it is robbed of sense and turned from its proper path by all sorts of failings and dis-orders—and also because man, who should assist it to achieve the fulfilment of its nature, works to destroy it under the secret direction of Satan, through original and actual sin. But this world is nonetheless always the world God created, the world in which the God of love is always active, the world of the angels, the future city of God, the world which is redeemed because at a particular moment in its history—not just any moment, but one preparing from far off the scientific and technological age of the West—God, unwilling to infringe our perverted freedom, came into the world to die, for love, at the hand of man, and so answered all our doubts and questions.

All material and human values are ambiguous. Evolution and history have meaning and direction for the one who sweeps over millions of years; the same events are meaningless and purely haphazard for one looking at the details of individuals or species or civilizations. Both aspects are equally true if not equally important. It is a world of contradiction, and of mystery—which confirms our faith. Death and pain are ambiguous. They are so even for the biologist. They are unavoidable, and they are right and proper to the extent that they fulfil their biological functions and contribute to the harmony of the universe. But the pointless excess of pain and suffering, or the deaths of those who may or may not have run their course, and must leave a gap, these present grievous problems which call for the light of religion. The love of man and woman is ambiguous. Man and wife are caught between two biological functions both produced by evolution but sometimes working in opposite directions: the duty to reproduce and the duty to unite, in a world which seems to demand the limitation of the birth-rate and particular respect for the individuality of each partner. It is impossible to derive, either from biology or religion, an absolutely safe legalism which would dispense us from facing personally all the difficult problems of our lives, our own problems and those of mankind.

So whether the world is regarded under its positive or under its negative aspects, it presents a picture in which science and religion are complementary. Such a complementarity, which is neither lazy compromise nor wishful thinking, has undeniable value in apologetics. The world of religion is the same world as that which science assures us is the real world. An apologetics which starts from science can do no more. Such a coming together of science and religion will be for some only a shock to their materialism, which will produce a greater open-mindedness, a broader agnosticism, more tolerance. It will make others suddenly aware of an aspect of the world of which they had been unaware. Christians, who sometimes have greater need of certitude, will see it as an astonishing agreement between the ascending reflection of the synthesis of the sciences and the descending reflection of theology reflecting on the world. They will become impervious to all atheist scientific apologetics; they will understand their religion better; above all, they will learn to love scientific explanation, which is just as evocative of true mystery; they will come in toleration and in the understanding of a truth that has several faces, to join with non-Christians in fruitful work for the advancement of knowledge, and for the fulfilment of man's task. To make scientific materialism into mystical materialism is to cling to the creation, to recognize the mysterious will of the Master of matter; he, to remain with us, to unite himself closer to us, chose the appearance of bread and the physical eating of the Eucharist, that sacrament opening for us such perspectives on the metaphysical mystery of being.

CHAPTER IX

THE TRUE AND FALSE LIMITS OF SCIENCE

SCIENCE AND PHILOSOPHY

Anyone who expects a scientist who is a Christian to produce absolute proofs of religious truths may find the preceding chapter disappointing, despite its scientific objectivity. The reason is that it is not our task in this book to write a treatise on apologetics or develop all the arguments for believing,[1] but simply to deal with the relations between science and religion. Scientific cosmology is not part of apologetics; the latter uses its arguments, and all scientific arguments as it uses all others, in support of the faith. It is not science which has to prove God's existence, but the science of the proofs of God's existence, which uses arguments borrowed from science alongside of those drawn from elsewhere. This is not the place to develop all the rational philosophical arguments which support the faith, nor to discuss their value. Nor is it the place to look at all the arguments from revelation, or to draw on mystical psychology to discover what experimental certitudes might emerge, or to discuss the manifold relations between psychiatry and mysticism.

We simply need to insist that it is a mistake, a scientific mistake, to think that man can have no certitude, no knowledge, except what he finds by way of the experimental sciences. It is equally mistaken to assume that the Christian need do

[1] That is the purpose of *Why We Believe*, by Léon Cristiani, in this series

no more than oppose theological dogmas, the rational faith taught by the Church, to the scientific account of the world. This would be to neglect the enormous intermediate field covered by philosophy. It is worth remembering that Aristotle, who understood so well, through his hylomorphism, the relations between mind and body, understood very little (certainly less than Democritus) about the physiology of the brain; while Descartes, who knew so much about neurology and reflexes and so on, utterly misunderstood those same relations. This supports the idea of a truth of philosophy which is independent, an idea often overlooked in this scientific and technological age, which is tolerant enough of fideism but objects to deep philosophical reflection on the essences of things. Such objection is excusable, since philosophy has often lost itself in a verbalism utterly unrelated to the world, and also because there are so many philosophical schools holding completely contradictory views. From this we should not infer that philosophy is incapable of arriving at the truth, but only that philosophy also is interdependent, not autonomous. The philosopher's task is to reflect on, to think about, reality. Reality has two aspects, religious and scientific. To achieve a synthesis of science and religion calls for the work of a philosopher who is willing to be in harmony with science and with religion together, while always remaining in harmony with reason. So it is for the philosopher to concern himself with God and with the soul's immortality, while taking into account what both science and religion have to say. Apologetics is essentially philosophical reflection. The scientist as such is therefore not concerned with it in detail. Yet he should insist on the importance and value of such reflection, so that, when he is simply unwilling to go beyond the bounds of his competence or his subject, he is not accused of treating philosophy as of no value. Science cannot directly prove the existence of God or the immortality of the soul. But this does not mean that the only alternative is to believe blindly whatever the Church says: we can by reflection attain to the truths of religion and their rationality. For the Catholic, "the faith" means more or less always not religious feeling or adherence to dogmas, but spiritualistic philosophical reflection.

Philosophy is twofold: one process of reflection ascending from the world overlaps a process of reflection on the same world descending from God and spiritual values. So there are two possible cosmologies, one from reflection on science, the other from the metaphysical analysis of reality in harmony with the faith. These two different methods can lead to a fruitful agreement.

If, because of the specializations of men, there must be scientists, philosophers, theologians and so on, in fact we all, if we want to understand the world and our religion, must do a little science, a little philosophy, a little theology; we must have a culture which is scientific, philosophical and theological, not simply a slight acquaintance with science, unsupported by philosophical reflection, set against some rather vague memories of the catechism. The world is one: we have many and various views of it: they have to be brought together and unified.[2] It is very difficult to separate out in our own conception of the world what we have taken from science, what from philosophy, and what from religion. Our belief does not stem from this or that particular argument, but from a whole collection of facts which have for us a much greater co-efficient of certitude because of the fact that they have been gathered into one coherent body.

Today more than ever the philosopher must take science into account. It offers him a vast number of small facts, and leaves him free to interpret them. But it also offers him a general, coherent picture of the world, and that picture makes some philosophical ideas obsolete.[3] We have seen that science

[2] It would be interesting to go into the methodological analogies between scientific and philosophical research. Rémy Collin insisted on the relationship between scientific, philosophical and religious certitude.

[3] Pius XII said: "Today, Catholic theologians should be able to count on our sons who are scientists and technologists, philosophers and lawyers, historians, sociologists and doctors, to provide their work with foundations in established secular knowledge. That is your privileged mission, in your quality as intellectuals, in the bosom of the Church." (Message to *Pax Romana*, August 1st, 1950.)

has condemned the old mechanistic materialism; the same is true of Cartesian dualism, of the separate soul acting on the body from without. The only ideas science can now tolerate on this question of the relations between soul and body are those of dialectical materialism and of Aristotelian or Thomist hylomorphism. There is no great limitation for the philosophers, really, for very different superstructures can be raised on the same foundations. It might be said that St Thomas, building on Aristotle's hylomorphism, yet preserved all that he received from Plato and St Augustine.

There is no such thing as pure science unmixed with philosophy. One small fact is not science. Science gathers facts into theories, and tries to make a picture of the world making action possible. Science is not only fruitful analysis: it must also be synthesis, an attempt to reconstitute reality. This aspect of science is sometimes neglected by some scientists, but it is nonetheless of the highest importance. Biology, a synthetic science which cannot forget the integrated wholeness of the creature under dissection, is especially aware of this. The attempt at synthesis goes beyond the specialized level of the various sciences and aims at producing a scientific picture of the world, a cosmology. At once it is a matter of philosophy, and the scientist giving himself to this task should have a philosophical mind. But it is very elementary philosophy, more scientific than philosophical, better left to the specialist philosopher of science, who is most competent to deal with it. The time is past when each specialist scientist could stay in his own subject and know nothing of sciences related to his own. Before that time, the scientist was a universal man; now that is no longer possible either. So some have to strive to break down the barriers. They are not approved of, and are accused of poaching others' territory, but what they do is most valuable: work in such subjects as cybernetics and information theory, crossing as they do the frontiers between the physical and the biological sciences, will end by abolishing the barriers.

The neurophysiologist has a special part to play in making this synthesis, since he is the specialist concerned with the organ of thought itself. It is possible to study the physiology of the brain without being interested in anything more than the microphysiology of nerve impulses and excitations and their inhibition; such analysis is extremely useful, since it examines the phenomena which make thinking possible. The neurophysiologist can never discover thought or consciousness themselves in the material records of their apparatus. Nor can the philosopher explain how the brain thinks. If progress is to be made, the neurophysiologist must not be afraid to develop a psychological and philosophical neurophysiology, with the intention of understanding how the brain, with its integration of elementary mechanisms, makes it possible for us to think, be conscious, and act. The neurophysiologist is a man: he knows, by introspection, that he has a "within", that he thinks, is conscious, reflects, is free, and judges his own conduct as good or bad, virtuous or vicious. His clear duty is not just to accept all this as the rest of men do, but to ask the technical question, How is all this possible in the brain? Of course, he cannot in this way grasp the essence of mind, or of consciousness; he cannot replace the psychologist or the philosopher. But he can construct a useful science of the cerebral mechanisms of thought. It is no longer possible now for science merely to study the external aspects of behaviour, or superficially examine the centres of action: it must discover all the internal mechanisms of motivation, it must understand the needs which are to be fulfilled.

The possibility of objective scientific study of subjectivity has been denied, and it is true that we cannot objectify a state of mind. But we can grasp its cerebral machinery. The functioning of the brain is the physiological aspect of the mental "within", and the conflicts between the conscious and the unconscious mind with which psycho-analysis deals are beginning to bring us some understanding of their cerebral aspect, of the battles of excitation and inhibition of nerve cells.

Despite the opposition of their ideologies, Pavlov usefully objectified whatever truth there was in the discoveries of Freud. Ideas of standards and values have nothing to do with a science knowing only isolated phenomena. But a doctor may judge the functional value of an organ, and we may be able to judge the value, in human terms, of behaviour in terms of the normal standards of the functioning of the brain. Human biology, as the science of a being who can form himself according to his nature or deform himself, produces the distinction between the normal and the pathological. It would be illusory to try to discover what in such a synthesis is science and what is philosophy. A man who refused to know himself could not analyse himself scientifically. But it is true that such an attempt is far from the usual work of a philosopher, and also that his field cannot be restricted to this construction of a scientific cosmology. His true task as a philosopher is to grasp that scientific cosmology firmly, a cosmology which seems materialist and dialectical, and penetrate to its deepest essence, to find again there the immanence of spirit. It is because Marxism is pure cosmology that it is utterly insufficient for the knowledge of being; it was because Teilhard de Chardin was scientific that he did not take to justifying his Christian evolutionism philosophically and ontologically. Christian philosophers must carry on this work of making a scientific synthesis which opens the way to religion. The biologist recognizes the fact of integration. The philosopher analyses the integrated being to discover what makes it integrated, the material and spiritual principles. He distinguishes the proper natures of the animal and the human soul. He asks what are the relations of man and the world with God, and in analysing the creative act he penetrates ever more intimately into the knowledge of God. If science seems to harmonize with religion, even almost to provide it with proofs, it is because reflective philosophical analysis opens wide paths joining scientific cosmology and metaphysics. And at the point where the scientist and the atheist philosopher must stop and doubt, unable to climb any higher, the Christian philosopher sees stretching before him the ways of religion, perfectly linked with the ascending paths of scientific philosophy and its ontological complement.

To understand and to explain the world, we need science,

and, as we have said, there is no reason to set out the limits of its proper field. But we do need to recognize the natural insufficiencies and incapabilities of science, which cannot exceed the potentialities of its method, the analysis and synthesis of being taken under its material aspect. Beyond this science has no competence, and we must look to the science of being itself, to metaphysics. To recognize this is already to turn towards religion.

SCIENCE AND ETHICS

The material and spiritual reality we are sensible of not only involves truth, but has other aspects. For example, it involves goodness and beauty, moral and aesthetic reality. And moral and aesthetic knowledge, which cannot be ignored without seriously mutilating man's nature, also have manifold relations with science. No kind of scientific philosophy can draw goodness and beauty in all their wholeness into science. So some have satisfied themselves by reducing them to emotional and subjective phenomena having nothing to do with truth. It would be interesting, moreover, to define exactly the difference between the thoroughgoing relativism of some rationalist philosophers for whom axiology, "the science of worth" (goodness) has nothing to do with epistemology, the science of knowledge (truth), and the more diversified opinion of the Marxist, who professes a morality or an aesthetic socialist realism having certain scientific aspects. These things raise problems analogous to those raised by the relations between science and religion.

We have already suggested how the biological knowledge of human beings can, in the field of ethics, enable us to define human nature, and pathological deviations from a norm. "Biological morality" has had a bad press for a long time,[4] since it was really a matter of an amoral, naturalistic ethics based on a number of biological facts of minor importance which were

---

[4] In fact, there is no more a biological morality than there is a biological metaphysics; it is a matter of the contribution of biology to ethics.

not specifically human, not on the biological knowledge of human nature as such. Such were the "might is right" morality, based on natural selection; racialism, based on mistaken ideas of genetics; such too was Kinsey's ignoring the distinction between normal and abnormal in the realm of sexual behaviour, his neglect of the principal characteristic of the brain in this matter, the possibility of a balanced control in true continence. When anyone speaks of a "morality without sin", we are dealing with a new variation on the same theme. Every sin is thought of as a pathological act of a sick brain, which is at the mercy of determinisms which suppress its freedom and produce a false and morbid sense of guilt. It is enough, therefore, to cure the sick man by biological or psychological therapeutics, and he will no longer be a sinner. Pope Pius XII, in his Christmas message of 1956, rightly spoke out against such a way of looking at it, which is very much the same as the Marxist's idea that deviations of conscience have a purely social origin. He showed how mistaken a notion of man it implied: man is defined as having a free choice between good and evil, and cannot be likened to a machine which is passive and simply goes wrong and then needs putting right again, like an animal treated by a veterinary surgeon. To cure a man appeal must be made to conscience, and there must be education in freedom. Psycho-analysis rightly insists on the dangers of the sort of education in which a false morality produces repressions and throws the individual mind out of balance. But psycho-analysis, too, errs by omission and falls into the same pseudo-biological way of looking at morality. It is not enough simply not to have repressions. It is just as unbalancing to give the instincts free rein, which cannot produce a normal personality knowing its own limits. So a kind of education is needed which will produce a balance, and which will avoid the dangers both of repression and of licence by ensuring that what is morally necessary is understood and accepted.

The Church has always rightly insisted that morality has its natural aspect: there is a natural morality, natural to man, explicable at the metaphysical level by the full understanding of the true nature of man and of the relations of man's soul with God. There is no morality without God. But it is too hasty to infer straight to "no morality without explicit reference to God". With morality, as with the laws of physics, the case is the same. Both are parts of God's creation, but they can be studied objectively in themselves and for themselves with no regard to metaphysics. Ethics is an autonomous human science, autonomous meaning no more than it does in the case of other sciences, independent. It is for metaphysics to provide the essential justification of ethics; it is for religion to give it its supernatural quality, to crown wisdom with sanctity. But the ethical philosopher as such is concerned with human behaviour and its evaluation, and must look for standards and for rules demanding the obedience of all men, whatever their creed.[5] Whether a man is Christian or not, he has a soul in a certain relationship to God: his duties are those of all men. Need one be a Christian to recognize those duties? The question is extremely important today, for we are at a turning-point in the history of civilization. Scientific progress has made it possible to mould man as we will, and man is very malleable; what sort of man do we want to produce? Should he belong to this or that kind of culture? Which is desirable, conformism or radicalism? Ethical thinkers do not all agree. The morality they outline is generally purely descriptive, and they infer from the variability of man's behaviour from age to age and from people to people that there is no morality common to all men. Marxists are alone in perceiving, with their idea of direction in history, any progress or direction in morality. So, generally, men claim the freedom to behave as their philosophy or religion requires. So there are many moral theories, and perverts who find themselves persecuted by society demand freedom for themselves. Such relativism is disastrous educationally. Chil-

---

[5] The existence of such rules is the basis of the moral absolute but their application to particular cases is a matter for research. The Church condemns any "particular moralities", but not the cautious and proper application of morality to particular cases.

dren have to be given a morality common to all philosophical schools. In practice there is often general agreement about social behaviour, as being good or bad. But apart from any absolute standard given by religion, it is impossible to justify one's own judgement.

It is therefore extremely important to understand what implications for morality biology may contain. It is not a matter of transforming the biologist into a moral philosopher. But we do have to use the arguments suggested by the biologist's reflection on man and his historical development as species and as an individual. Just as the Christian can be given some idea by his religion of what he ought to do, so every man can be given some idea by biology of what he must do if he wants to be and to stay normal. In both cases, if the precepts given demand man's use of his freedom, they cannot destroy that freedom. This is not the place to work out this kind of biological ethical theory, adapted to the true psycho-biological nature of man. But we can stress the extraordinary agreement between true Christian ethics (not Pharisaism) and what human biology can suggest, when the two are brought together, as an agreement perceptible to all men. The chief implications of Christian ethics, considering what man is biologically, are very important in the field we are now concerned with, that of the relations between science and religion.

This biological ethics, which is linked in its historical development with the story of the evolution of man, is an ethics, above all, of the functioning of man's brain. It considers the brain as the instrument of man's freedom, and so seeks to discover what makes the exercise of that freedom possible. If there are biological and psychological processes of a purely physical nature which can rob a man of his freedom by making the brain abnormal, true biological ethics is concerned with the normal brain, which has not lost its freedom, and with the question, What ought the individual to do to stay normal and free? So it is not a matter of nursing a sick man in order to cure him, but of advising a normal man in his free behaviour. If this is so, sin will seem to be the pathological behaviour of a normal individual who is misusing his brain, knowingly or not, and who can fall into the habit of doing so and become abnormal and come into the category of the sick. One cannot so imitate pathology with impunity. A whole cerebral "hygiene" of behaviour can be developed, which directs conduct, within its freedom, towards precisely those physical processes which make man human and free, and which are moral and virtuous when issuing as behaviour. It is possible to define the patterns of behaviour which are best and most truly profitable both to the individual and to society. The unleashing of the instincts and the emotions, whether of sexuality or aggressiveness, inhibits the use of the more highly developed, specifically human, parts of the brain: only the lower centres, common to men and the animals, are used. In the same way, a man who does not use his own judgement and freedom, being entirely ruled by conformity to custom, even if he is wholly adjusted to the society he has adapted himself to, is not behaving fully as a man. To be fully human is to use to the maximum man's capacities for judgement and for unrest: to use the pre-frontal brain, specific to man, which enables man to know his needs and his limits, and to recognize his place, among other men, one person among others, in a social relationship based on love. The oppressor and the oppressed are both abnormal. A man is only balanced, biologically, so far as his brain is concerned, if he exists in that optimum state between anarchy and complete constraint: neither tyrant or idol, nor thing. The eudemonist ethics proposed by Teilhard de Chardin puts this psycho-biological balance clearly: "Centralization on oneself, decentralization on others, supercentralization on One greater than oneself."[6] Surely the best conditions for true balance lie in the relations of man with an ideal who is a Person? It has been shown by Daim that neuroses can bring about the idolization of a human being who is then put in the place of God. From a strictly physiological point of view, then, we can say that Gide's or Sartre's idea of a freedom without meaning, or not "involved", is quite wrong, since there is for man no free-

[6] Published in *Table ronde*, 90.

dom as such. His freedom is the voluntary adherence to a higher moral process which sets him free. The relationship of this idea to Marxism is plain. But Marxism is seriously wrong in its failure to recognize either the freedom of the individual or what it is that sets one free.

When biological and religious ethics come to such agreement and make one system, it may be possible one day to judge conduct and assess political ideas considering not simply the material advantage of a individual or class, but what is favourable and, from the point of view of humanity, advantageous, both for the progress of each individual man and for the humanization of society. The service of man and the interests of humanity will become of first importance: today, despite the lip-service paid to these ideas, contempt for the individual man and his freedom seems almost the only common feature of our various forms of society—which the Church recognizes so well when she opposes both Communism and capitalism.

SCIENCE AND BEAUTY

When a scientist is called a poet, as Teilhard de Chardin has been, it may be a compliment to his style, but it is more likely a fierce and bitter criticism. Not all scientists have the ability he had of so wonderfully expressing their feelings before the beauty of the world, but they are all sensible of it. If they are not, it is not just a human quality they lack, but an essential quality of the scientist. Here, as before, we must draw a distinction without enforcing separation. The object of science and of scientific method has nothing to do with aesthetic knowledge. The scientist as such is not a poet, nor an artist, nor a composer. But, on the other hand, the scientist, like every other man and perhaps more so than other men, is endowed with aesthetic sensibility; and on the other, science, as the knowledge of a reality which is one and beautiful, is bound to come into contact with beauty. And beauty is not a superfluous, irrational thing, but an essential element of that aspect of the creation which transcends reason. Analysis may isolate the beauty of every humble detail; giving a flower a scientific name adds nothing to its beauty, but the detailed and profound examination necessary to give that name reveals at its very heart structures and harmonies beyond the profane eye of fact. The world of the microscope has a strange beauty of its own. But there is more than the beauty of detail: there is the beauty of the whole, the beauty of a theory, of the whole scientific picture, of the world understood and explained by science. Beauty is not a sure sign of truth. A simple construction of our minds can be beautiful. Yet aesthetic feeling is sometimes the sign of that profound concord between our ideas and things which is itself an indication of the spiritual basis of all creation.

Some have tried to set aesthetic knowledge over against scientific knowledge. That is a mistake. Not only is there the beauty of the work of science; there is the relationship between the results of each form of knowledge. Aesthetic knowledge, and especially that of the poet, seizes by some kind of intuition, at once, the synthetic and spiritual nature of being, what is most essential to it; it does not destroy, it communes with being. Analytical scientific knowledge is apparently the opposite. It labours, so it seems, to break down that wholeness which is beautiful. But when science in its synthetic process then reconstitutes the whole, now understood in all its parts, an image somewhat surprisingly emerges from the abstract work of the scientist which is more exact but lacks none of the elements of that which the eye of the artist took in at a glance in his intuition. There is an ambiguity in the knowledge of the artist as in that of the scientist, for, like the latter, the artist knows joy, harmony and beauty only in the gap between desire and what is desired, in the hopeless search for an ineffable absolute. Surely there is a close kinship between the experimental effort of the artist desirous of expressing his feelings ever more fully, and that of the scientist?

A physiological critique of knowledge from a neurological point of view—the brain and the senses—would be as useful to the artist as to the scientist, in helping to appreciate how he is looking at the world, and the relation between that view and reality. Consider the harmonious agreement between ourselves and the world expressed in mathematics, with its astonishing powers. It is a closed and abstract poetry, a language of the brain, which yet describes reality so perfectly that the world is practically one great equation. The same agreement is found also, at its highest, in that art which is nearest to abstract science in its precision, and in its mystery nearest to the essence of the spiritual, to God: music. What is more moving, more significant of the unity of man's spirit, than to see learned and unlearned, civilized and primitive, at one in listening to Mozart?

But ordinary language is poor and insufficient when we would celebrate the union of science and beauty. The poet-scientist Pierre Termier found the right words for that lyrical flight which was the source of his vocation as a scientist:

> This passion of love which is the scientific vocation, this strange, superhuman passion, is unloosed in the heart of the scientist by the splendour he glimpses, by the Beauty he divines, by the simple reflection, come from far off, after a measureless journey through measureless darkness, of the Truth, which is clearly the final aim of our aspirations, the deepest need of our intelligence, the pole our life must be orientated on. The scientist is more sensible than his companions on the way to these reflections, these radiances, this light. He sees it, while to the majority it is still invisible; and once he has seen it, he cannot ever cease to see it. Like the antique statue which sounded when touched by the rays of the sun, the soul of the scientist moves and vibrates as soon as it is touched by any wave from the Infinite: and that emotion is always with him, not to be assuaged, and the vibration becomes a note, a hymn, an unceasing chant. He longs only to vibrate more, to feel more deeply, to gather to himself more of that light, to move closer to the mysterious source around which he desires to gravitate perpetually.

SCIENCE AND HUMANISM

The opinion is widely held that science is one-track and all-embracing, presenting us with a view of the world which is technological and dehumanized. It is not enough simply to reply by saying, quite correctly, that science only takes a partial view of the world. Since this partial view does take in the real world, science finds there, in its own field, arguments not lightly dismissed for the reality of aspects not its own. It is not for scientists to claim the specialist study of these aspects for themselves, but to point out the agreements between them and itself and to ask the other specialists dealing with man and the world to take them into account. Though specializing in his own branch of science, the scientist has to remain a whole man; it is indeed his only way of preserving his science from being distorted. In reality, what he has to establish is not a scientific picture of the world and man, but the contribution of science to the whole picture. Then he will not be tempted by his science, useful and necessary as it is, to undervalue reality or to reduce it to a machine, or even something producing itself by the interplay of natural forces. It is a world of complexity and mystery, and he is led quite naturally to the religious explanation of its harmonies and discords.

Can science really form the whole man? This question has occupied educationists for some time, and is of vital importance now, when more and more young people are every day turned towards a scientific education, because of the progress of science and technology. The usual reply to that question is based on the assessment of the present state of things, and is that science can supply us with knowledge and with a way of thinking directed to what is concrete and rational; that this is very valuable in education, but that although science may have something to contribute to traditional humanism, it is not itself one of the humanities. But we cannot leave it at that. Here too we should recognize that science has not been asked for all it has to give. This whole book should have shown that it is possible to derive one kind of humanism from science, that the tragedy now is that science has become all-powerful on the technological, dehumanizing side, but that its normative value as a mode of knowing has been neglected. Scientific humanism has yet to be constructed. It is all the more necessary that this should be done now when, in a world based on

science and technology, rules, restraints and standards can only
have their full value when brought into agreement with scientific knowledge of man and the world. If we want to prevent a
certain tendency of science to dehumanize man by treating him
as an object, we can only see such a practice done away with
by showing scientifically that man is a subject, who is destroyed
if he is not considered as such. Science is not neutral, indifferent
to good and evil: in the objective judgement it brings to bear
on the word and man, it distinguishes normal and pathological.
But man is, of course, always at liberty to take no account
of this, and to misuse science.

The failing of our scientific teaching is not simply quantitative; that can be, and is being, put right. What gives us more
and more uneducated and more and more dehumanized technologists is the qualitative failure, the old-fashioned refusal,
based on the idea of metaphysical neutrality, to look scientifically
at man as a whole. All levels of education ought to include
science, not out of curiosity about nature, nor as way of learning to think, but as an approach to self-knowledge. It is not
only scientists and technologists who need the scientific picture
of man, but every man, both for himself and for his future in
society. A basic education in normative human biology ought
to be created. It is particularly necessary that intending
specialists in the humanities in Arts faculties should receive a
scientific introduction to biology and mathematics, especially
statistics. Such a course is no less necessary to intending philosophers and theologians. Is it right that doctors should know
only man's material body, and the pathological deviations of
his mind? How can lawyers, writers, politicians, engineers,
be balanced human beings, if they have no scientific knowledge of man?

But if the teaching of science can go seriously astray in the
direction of pure technology, there is another danger for the
future: scientific humanism may become a closed, all-embracing system, self-sufficient and shut in on itself, excluding other
values, opposed to traditional humanism and to religion.
Specialists in the sciences of man sometimes want to form a

separate faculty of their own. Let us hope they do not there develop into "mind mechanics", treating man simply as an object, and losing all idea of an absolute. Such men should not only learn from human biology about chromosomes and the nervous system and hormones: they should understand through it how complex man is and what he is, and they should discover the real meaning of the history of his development, to rescue them from the false relativism in which they are lost because of their pseudo-objectivity, which ignores all standards. Specialists in the sciences of man are scientists: they should not, then, so cut themselves off from all philosophy as to become mere technicians. But it is also necessary for the philosophers to construct their philosophy—without changing its essence—with the scientific picture of the world in mind.

There are not two cultures, one literary and one scientific. There is one human culture, approached by various ways. The less education is partitioned, the more obvious that will be. What is needed is a humanist education including science and history, as a basis for a technological education directed towards the biological or the mathematical sciences or to grammatical studies. Today, a fundamentally humanist education no longer exists. All that is left of the humanities is a literary technique. There was a time when literary men such as John Evelyn and John Dryden, both Fellows of the Royal Society, could and did keep abreast of developments in the natural sciences of their time. Despite the progress of science, we have to get back to that. For that, we shall have to know how to sift out what is absolutely necessary, and, while passing over details, keep in all that is valuable.[7]

Scientific humanism must stop being a piece of artillery against the classical humanist tradition. Without the latter, it stultifies itself and is no longer truly humanist. It becomes then only narrow scientific rationalism. It is really the contribution made by science—by philosophical reflection on

[7] It is worth remarking with approval the increase in and success of "popular" science; so long as it is well done. It is a duty of the Christian scientist.

science—to the knowledge of the whole man. It is an aspect of that knowledge complete in itself and unrestricted, but not closed to other aspects, the necessity and value of which it can itself recognize.

But why want to know? Some scientists, like Pierre Termier, have rightly sung the joy of knowing, the almost religious joy of participating more fully in the work of the creation. Others have celebrated the complementary aspect, the joy of mastery, of conquering. This is not just the joy of feeling one's own power, but the joy of serving the creation and helping towards its goal, the joy of doing one's job and being useful to mankind. The Marxists are right to insist on *praxis*. It is this insistence on action which has been behind the triumph of the West. Action and meditation should not be opposed to each other; Christianity and science are agreed in putting the two together in a harmonious balance, as opposed to certain eastern mysteries. When we see the miseries of the poor villagers of India or Africa, we can see the importance of scientific progress in the struggle against such wretchedness. That progress must not dehumanize men culturally, not take away any essentials from older civilizations. But the importance of science for the happiness of man should not be underrated.

There is a good deal of truth in the old scientific rationalist's optimism. It is not a matter of a temptation to a Promethean revolt against the gods, to change the nature or condition of men. It is a matter of the ordinary duty of man in the part given him by God, who put his creation in man's hands. What is wrong is to believe in a sort of automatic progress produced by a purely technical science: that would be to hold that technology and science always advance towards good; it would also be to lose oneself in the trees and lose sight of the wood. There is a dreadful ambiguity about words such as progress, profit, interest, advantage, which are generally regarded with reference to values which are relative—a given individual or social group, or the future of mankind. True science shows us the meaning of the human person, and lays down the conditions for his full development. And that person must be put back in the centre of all things as the first and fundamental point of reference. There is no such thing as that frigid entity, humanity. There are only men. And if we ought to think of men to come, who should receive greater blessings than we have, yet we ought not to forget our contemporaries. Men cannot be advanced, cannot advance, in happiness except in freedom; that is, in the recognition of their true duty, which is not total sacrifice of self, but full self-achievement within limitations which are balanced and which produce harmony. There is no progress or advantage other than that which is in the interests of and advantageous for the full development of men, of men and their relationships, which constitute society. Of every technological step forward we should ask, whether it is true progress or not; and we should use it only so far as it is humanizing. Atomic or psycho-biological techniques should be regarded not solely with their possibilities in mind but looking at the value to man of those possibilities. To be able to control and use more and more energy is necessary to man's future well-being; but the production of that energy must not involve the risk of so seriously disturbing the environment as to render it unfit for human life. There is no need to lament the passing of the good old days when men died of wretchedness and poverty; but there is no need either for the technological age to create worse troubles than those of the age it succeeds. The fundamental problem of our age is to produce a morality common to all men in order to control technological progress. We do not want pessimism, nor a complacent optimism, but realism as to what has to be done. As we have seen, scientific humanism, with its possible normative function, provides perhaps the only immediately acceptable control, to humanize progress and make it the progress of man. Great social or economic or political theories about under-privileged people or classes are not of great fundamental importance. What is needed is to change their inhuman state. Science can define man's natural conditions and set out the ways to realize them. It is science which is really revolutionary, which forces us to go forward to a better civilization and greater freedom (for example, by automation), until the actualization of a society without classes but not without some functional differences according to needs and aptitudes.

No scientist today can live in an ivory tower, a closed laboratory. He should not be the blind servant of the politician, but is bound to keep an eye open for the applications of scientific advances. The physicists are ultimately responsible for all the consequences, for good or ill, of atomic energy: Einstein's torment of mind is well known. In the many decisions he has to make, the advice, not of the technologist but of the scientific humanist in harmony with Christian humanism, is essential to the statesman endeavouring to serve his fellow-men. The politician is autonomous, but his autonomy and his possible choices are limited by his dependence on humanity.

The word "humanism" has for a long time had overtones of atheism. It has meant the exaltation of man against the so-called bonds of religion. No one now disputes that Christianity is a kind of humanism. In fact, there are no more two or more humanisms than there are two moralities. Scientific and Christion humanism are agreed on all that is essential in man, and lead to the same decisions, the same actions. This man, who is set in the centre of the picture, is indeed the high point of evolution, and bound to manifest the possibilities of his nature. To refer everything to man is not to lull oneself with what is purely relative: it is to base oneself on what is essential—the soul and God—even if one does not recognize all the true meaning of values and of transcendence. Man, who does not invent values, is of the highest value when he considers himself as an end; but he is also of the highest value in God's eyes, as the end of creation, and in that he should find his true meaning. Perfect man is not an ideal, a utopian idea, but a fact already achieved which guarantees our efforts: for at a certain point in history God was made man to show us what man really is.

So this inquiry into the relations between science and religion should end with an appeal to men to unite in the service of man as a creature of God. There must be a science no longer even possibly opposed to religion, nor wishing to be separated from it, but bound to work with religion, with mutual respect for each other's viewpoint, to assure a happy future for mankind. Not an exclusive science, a world shut in on itself, but a world open to all reality, in which science discovers mysterious structures which only need to be fitted into a metaphysical explanation; provided only that we do not restrict ourselves to the immanent. Science and religion must get together and work together. As Teilhard de Chardin said: "Without the infusion of some new blood, Christianity runs the risk of weakening and losing itself in the clouds; and yet more certainly, without the infusion of some principle of universal love, man with his sense of progress will shudder away in horror of the frightening cosmic machine he finds himself involved in."

Love is the supreme value, the highest power: is it not there in the dream of social justice of the scientific rationalist? The organic conditions of and the necessity for man's harmonious balance have been objectified by the physiology of the brain and by social psychology. What humble men, ordinary men, men of feeling, so long scorned by the rationalists, have always asserted, the superiority of the heart over the reason, this is nowadays practically scientifically proved. Not opposition between heart and reason: but that love is the only true power of knowledge man has, in the exalted union of emotion and narrow, but necessary, reason.

The world of science and technology will only be saved if it becomes the world of the technique, the brain-technique, of being truly and freely human. "To love one's neighbour as oneself" may well become the golden rule of psychology and of scientific sociology.

The scientist is not haughty and disdainful and aloof, the high priest of a mysterious new religion. He is a man of facts, labouring at research which is often fruitless. He should be humble. He knows that the beatitude about "the poor in spirit" has nothing to do with ignorance but with the pride and self-sufficiency of the man who thinks he knows everything. His patron saint is always, more than all the philosophers honoured by the Church, the humble friar of Assisi, who sang creation's praises so magnificently while suffering in his own flesh the Passion of Christ. With his own science and religion harmoniously balanced, he has his place in an ordinary parish church; but he can nonetheless be proud and happy that some of his colleagues have been able to combine a scientific and a religious vocation. What a joy it is for the Catholic scientist to assist at a Mass sung by a scientist-priest who introduces in the most solemn prayer of offering and adoration the whole world of science and technology, with all its concerns and cares.

CHAPTER X

CONCLUSIONS

We have now arrived at a simple and honest "No" in answer to the question implied in the title of this book. We arrived at this negative not because of an *a priori* assertion of the certitude of religion, but by considering the meaning of science and that of religion as compared with one another, and by showing that neither excluded the other. There is no need to under-estimate the tremendous importance of science both for know-ledge and for action. Pope Pius XII, a man of his own times and of all popes the most concerned about science, unceasingly stressed that importance. There is no need to modify science so as to be able to force spirituality in to fill up the gaps in the explanation, nor to alter it by sketching a spiritualistic picture of science unacceptable to scientists who are not Catholics. The point is that science itself, the real science of all scientists, that common power which is not truly neutral, does not neces-sarily lead to agnosticism. Scientific rationalists and Marxists may think that science opposes and destroys religion. They believe this because they have a false notion of religion; because in their ignorance of philosophy they confuse the phenomeno-logical level of scientific explanation with the ontological level of metaphysics, since they oppose metaphysics and its appar-ently dialectical actualization; because they confuse acting and thinking matter with a matter which would think for and in itself. Their belief is far from the truth: science describes for us a picture of the world and man very much in line with religious values. To oppose science and religion; to be agnostic and narrowly restrict man's potentialities; to reduce religion to feel-ing; to separate two realms of being, that of science—matter—

and that of religion—spirit; to do all this one must be scientifically and religiously uneducated. But is not this one of the most marked characteristics of contemporary life, among non-Christians and, alas! Christians alike? In a technological and scientific world, especially when the claims of science are not exaggerated, a merely rudimentary knowledge of science is very dangerous for an uninstructed faith. If we form for ourselves childish images of God and of the relations between soul and body, a very few arguments from the theory of evolution or from neurology will be enough to destroy our faith. The grace of faith is a talent we are bound to increase. Preserving a living and personal faith is quite a different thing from sticking to a faith which is part of the society in which one lives, and in which everyone believes. To avoid the destruction of our faith by science, we must put it out of the reach of science, not by finding it some secret hiding place, but by making it a real part of our total experience of the world. Every layman has the duty, not to be a controversial theologian, but to be instructed in theology; and it is the duty of every theologian to explain how unchangeable doctrines can be reconciled with the scientific picture of the world. Nursing and improving one's faith demands considerable philosophical thought about science: what precisely does it imply? Only so can we discover its spiritual implications.

It is no longer possible for any man today, on this small planet, bombarded with news by radio and newspapers, to dream of taking shelter in an ivory tower. From a very early age, whatever their race or their social class or their education, all are subject to the impact of the material world and the materialist bias of scientific explanation. Christians must therefore be prepared for it. Very soon missionaries in Asia and Africa will find themselves faced with but one problem; Marxism is above all scientific propaganda used against religion. To be one of the Chinese today, Fr Lebbe would have to have the mind of a Teilhard de Chardin.

Two mistakes must be avoided: we must neither despise science in the name of religion, as having all the answers, nor must we argue with the scientist on his own ground. That is, we must not refute scientific facts or theories, however easily refuted they may be, in the name of Christian doctrine. On the contrary, we ought sympathetically to consider all that our opponent says in order to find, if we can, the interpretation which is reconcilable with the faith, by distinguishing the two ways of looking at one and the same world. Nothing is more effective in making him more tolerant and open-minded than accepting his scientific arguments, even encouraging him to develop them further and to improve his scientific explanation; for this should make it easier for him to perceive spiritual values in their physical, natural aspect. On the other hand, we should disabuse him of the false ideas he is forever constructing of the nature of religion. Our opponent is never entirely and absolutely wrong; we must start from the aspect of truth he grasps in order to bring him to the truth. It is sounder apologetics to show a materialist all the consequences of his materialism which can lead him towards religion, than simply to point out to him that his materialism cannot explain everything. In that way he will be led to see its failings for himself.

And there are two things we must firmly accept. First, that science and religion are two different approaches to reality, distinct in their methods of thought; so that science can offer no proofs in the field of religion, in either sense, scientific or religious. And second, that since there is but one reality, science is capable of grasping that the religious approach is possible, and so of opening and exploring the ways towards religion; while religion, since it is not apart from this world but in it, itself can move towards meeting science. Any opposition between the world and man, the realm of matter in which there are neither standards nor values, and God, the world of the spirit and spiritual values, is quite false. Yet it is on such opposition that the present conflict between materialism and spiritual philosophy, science and religion, depends. Materialism is thought to be a metaphysics of denial, whereas it really ought to be only explanation on the scientific, material level, and should, even at that level, encounter true values. Religion is thought to be the only defender of purely spiritual values, while those values really only exist in this world actually *in* this physical world. Religion gives us the real meaning of these values and of spirituality in themselves, by connecting them with the transcendence of God. But, even without religion, it is possible to arrive at them in their natural, physical aspect, and here there is no room for disagreement between men. Spiritual philosophers should be persuaded of the coherence and the apparent autonomy of the world as aspects of the immanence of spirit; they should distinguish spirit from matter, but not separate it completely from the world of matter; they should help non-Christians to perceive it, even if they cannot get them to understand its true nature. It is not possible to think of man rightly and truly without attributing to him the nature that religion postulates for him, setting him in relation to God; but his nature is partly accessible to the phenomenological method of science, not in its wholeness, but sufficiently to make possible the recognition of human values. In order to get rid of the natural aspect of man's spirit seen by the Christian, the materialist is forced to be wanting in realism, not to see man scientifically as he is. To see man scientifically as he is is not to prove the immortality of his soul, but to make room for the philosophical arguments which can prove it.

So we come, as always, to the need for philosophical reflection. Nothing would be further from the truth than to declare that now, as opposed to the position in 1900, there are no problems concerning the relations between science and religion. There are plenty of problems, and they have not all been solved, even if we do see better how they should be tackled: not by separating the two fields, but by distinguishing the two approaches to one and the same world, two approaches which must be harmonized without altering either. When science and religion are discussed today, it is no longer problems, but men who should be kept in mind, all the martyrs of eastern Europe and the Far East who because of Marxist scientific rationalism no longer have the right to practise their religion, or are merely tolerated as backward; we should think of all the young children who, deprived of the religious education necessary for faith, are subjected to a biased scientific education designed to prove that religion does not exist. When shall we be able to make Marxists understand that an atheism based on religious ignorance is neither rational nor valid; that if they really are working with, in the true direction of, history, their atheism will end not in the suppression of religion but in the clear possibility of a religion which is not alienated?

In order to bring the religious and the scientific approaches together in a unity which compels assent and attracts the free approval of our faith, we must first of all provide them with a common language. Most of the difficulties come from the fact that scientists and theologians do not mean the same thing by the same words. There is nothing in the scientific theory of evolution which the theologian should condemn as "evolutionism". It is quite enough, in bringing the two points of view together, simply to change some of the terms used, to tone down certain extravagances of expression, for agreement to be reached without difficulty. And nothing is more necessary than such conjunctions of the two viewpoints. How is the ordinary Christian to manage if scientists and theologians have not succeeded in presenting him with a synthesis acceptable both from the point of view of religion and from that of science? We need another St Thomas Aquinas. Philosophers, scientists and theologians have a good deal of work to do together before that synthesis is achieved. But even now the convergence and growing agreement of the two points of view is sufficient to reassure the Christian and to prevent the anti-religious misuse of science, provided an outmoded presentation of the unchangeable truths of religion is not allowed to upset it all.

Science explains, and religion explains; the world so explained is and will always be a world admitting of mystery, the true mystery of being, infinitely surpassing the petty failures of science. This is the difficulty: to maintain in spite of everything the possibility of mystery—which does not at all imply the possibility of magic. Far from everything being clear and definite and determined for one who understands religion and science together, there is plenty of room in the complexity of the world for the freedom of God, for miracles, for grace, for Providence, and for response to prayer. Prudence is needed when we are faced with unusual events. We should not assert as true facts we are not certain of, but nor should we declare them impossible, especially since, as we have said, rational explanation by no means rules out the intervention of God. If pathological conditions can produce hallucinations, they are produced by a mechanism of the brain; religion may also produce them—only now they are visions—by the same mechanism, in quite different physiological conditions. It is stupid to replace medicines by prayer, but the stupidity resides especially in reducing prayer to the status of a medicine. Prayer is of tremendous importance on the spiritual level, and as to this science has nothing to say; at the physical level the complexity of the causes required to arrive at a particular event is such that there is ample room for Providence to use coincidences. Providence, moreover, is not the disorganization of the universe in our service: it works above all through spiritual graces enabling us to draw some profit from any circumstances. Because of a remnant of positivism and scientific rationalism, the scientific mind is a little upset by any prayer that is not simply one of adoration or offering. His disquiet is wrong: in a world where everything is in God there is immense intersolidarity; but it is clearly rather the laws of creation in evolution bringing secondary causes to the fore which intervene. To declare that "if there were a good God, there would be no evil," is to have learnt nothing about science and nothing about God. Unfortunately it is a common remark.

It is difficult to be realistic; we all tend to oscillate between extreme pessimism and facile optimism. The true optimist knows all about evil and does all he can to redeem it. Whatever else it was, Teilhard de Chardin's work was not deceptively optimistic, the facile certitude that the harmony of science and religion would be produced simply by the automatic development of the noösphere. There is no such Utopia described in his work, since he always recognized, by his affirmation of the freedom of man, that to achieve the good our free agreement is needed. The world naturally has a fine and wonderful future: we can wreck that future.

If science and religion come together, their convergence has great value as apologetics. But we cannot leap to the conclusion that that would convert all non-believers; we cannot even conclude that that happy harmony would be part of the mental furniture of all Christian scientists. We must realize that that harmony is ideally possible; but we must also realize that we fall sometimes into that dark night where nothing exists but the certitude of faith. To separate the two fields would be an easy solution which might in some cases pose fewer problems, but it would be wrong, and an unstable solution. We can imagine the successive stages in the religious life of a Christian scientist who is frequently troubled in his faith by his scientific mental attitude.[1] This does actually happen, and we must be aware of it, so as to be able to defend ourselves against it. Even if we overcome that doubt and the temptation to split the one into many, how easy it is to be discouraged when we see how beautiful the world might possibly be today and look at what the freedom of men who will not understand has made of it, and even more when we see how far we ourselves, despite our clearer vision, belong in all our acts to this sinful world.

But the hardest cross for the Catholic scientist is the impossibility of bearing perfectly convincing witness to both science and religion: which is precisely the purpose of this book. He is split in two, belonging to two often hostile worlds, that of non-Christian scientists and that of the Church; and he feels that he belongs honestly and fully to both. He knows that his purpose in life is to bear witness among the scientists to the value and truth of his religion, and to bear witness among his co-religionists to the value of science and its compatibility with religion. To work as one, to be an apostle,

[1] This should not make us overlook the fact that the scientific context of his life can make easier for the Christian the perception of certain truths of the Christian message.

doubly an apostle, in the two worlds, to make scientific interpretation move towards religion and the formulations of spiritual philosophy move towards science, he must be recognized as belonging to them by each of the two worlds. Of course, it is useful and profitable for Catholic scientists to get together to define their positions with regard to difficult problems where physicists or biologists may not be agreed, but this will not in any way alter the fact that each belongs, as a scientist, to science, which is neutral and indifferent, and as a Christian, to his normal parish church. How distressing it is, when one has tried objectively to develop an idea of science more realistic than usual and more congruent with spiritual values, while remaining scientific and refusing to conjure up proofs of that God who is not doubtful to us, to be accused at the end by non-Christian scientists of being a fideist twisting science in the service of religion—an accusation which absolutely frustrates one's attempt at reaching agreement. And how distressing it is, when with great difficulty one tries to show Christians that science has a real explicative power quite in agreement with religion, to be told that one is a materialist if not a Marxist, trying to destroy religion, or that one is trying to change Christian doctrines, that one is Modernist or at least a liberal. And the distress is the greater because one knows what one was trying to do, because the synthesis is really possible: if it fails in this way, that is because of one's own failings, which must be made up by hard work and unceasing reflection.

Everywhere man finds frustration, suffering, death. The disciple is not above his Master: if the unity of the human and divine natures that Jesus Christ made in his own person brought him contradiction, persecution, and in the end, the Cross, then we should expect that the work of his disciples to conquer the various possessions of man by divine grace also brought and brings to them contradiction, persecution, and in the end, the Cross. Christ in all the fullness of his being is the pattern of the work of the Church in the midst of humanity; so the first temporal function of his mystical body will not be to bring about a state of harmony for man, but to accomplish the Passion of Christ. This does not mean that we have to speak of an irreconcilable split between the Church and the world, nor of tearing apart the activity of Christ's apostles once human values are introduced into the Christian universe. Pessimism is wrong here. The pessimist has no right to penetrate the mystery of the grief accompanying the Redemption, nor is he justified in cursing all that is earthly. But more than this, however paradoxical it may seem, we can assert that the Cross is actually on the side of the harmony, the synthesis of the human and the divine. The Cross makes actual, on a superhuman level it is true, the temporal unity, not the split, between the sinful world and grace. "The world is crucified to me, and I to the world," wrote St Paul (Gal. 6. 14). Let us acknowledge that there is no other way for the Christian apostle to take the world up into the divine system of existence. But this must not be taken as meaning that there is a divorce between the Christian and the world. In that saying of St Paul, we believe, is the most powerful and the most beautiful harmony that can be achieved in time, while we await the plenitude of the glory of eternal life.

SELECT BIBLIOGRAPHY

In this series: ABELÉ, Jean, S.J.: *Christianity and Science*; BORNE, Étienne: *Modern Atheism* (American edn. *Atheism*); CHAMBRE, Henri, S.J.: *Christianity and Communism*; LE TROCQUER, René: *What is Man?*

ALLERS, R.: *The Successful Error*, London and New York, Sheed and Ward, 1941.

AYER, A. J.: *Language, Truth and Logic*, London and New York, Oxford Univ. Press, 1936; *The Problem of Knowledge*, London, Macmillan, and New York, St Martins Press, 1956.

BALTHASAR, H. U. von: *Science, Religion and Christianity*, trans. by Hilda Graef, London, Burns and Oates, 1958.

BIVORT DE LA SAUDÉE, J. (Ed.): *God, Man and the Universe*, London, Burns and Oates, and New York, Kenedy, 1954.

BRIGHT, Laurence, O.P.: *Whitehead's Philosophy of Physics*, Newman Philosophy of Science Series, London and New York, Sheed and Ward, 1958.

CARREL, A.: *Man, the Unknown*, London, Hamish Hamilton, 1949, and New York, Harper, 1935.

DUBARLE, D., O.P.: *Scientific Humanism and Christian Thought*, trans. by R. Trevett, London, Blackfriars, 1956.

ENGELS, F.: *Dialectics of Nature*, trans. by C. Dutt, London, Lawrence and Wishart, and New York, International Publishers, 1940.

HALDANE, J. B. S.: *Marxist Philosophy and the Sciences*, London, Allen and Unwin, 1938.

HUXLEY, J. S.: *Man in the Modern World*, London, Chatto and Windus, and New York, New American Library, 1947; *Evolution in Action*, London and New York, Harper, 1953; *Religion without Revelation*, London, Parrish, and New York, Harper, 1957.

KEYNES, J. M.: "Newton the Man" in *Newton Tercentenary Celebrations*, Cambridge and New York, Cambridge Univ. Press, 1947.

MARITAIN, J.: *Redeeming the Time*, London, Sheed and Ward, and New York, Hillary, 1943.

RUSSELL, B.: *Mysticism and Logic*, New York, Barnes and Noble, 1954; *Why I am not a Christian, and other essays*, London, Allen and Unwin, and New York, Simons and Schuster, 1957.

RUSSELL, J., S.J.: *Science and Metaphysics*, Newman Philosophy of Science Series, London and New York, Sheed and Ward, 1958.

TAYLOR, F. Sherwood: *Two Ways of Life*, London, Burns and Oates, 1947; *Man and Matter*, London, Chapman and Hall, 1951; *Short History of Science and Scientific Thought*, New York, Norton, 1957; *The Century of Science*, London, The Scientific Book Club, 1943.

WHITE, V., O.P.: *God and the Unconscious*, London, Collins, 1952; *Soul and Psyche; an enquiry into the relationship of psychotherapy and religion*, London, Collins, 1960.

WIENER, P. P.: *Readings in the Philosophy of Science*, New York, Scribner, 1953.

The Twentieth Century Encyclopedia of Catholicism

The number of each volume indicates its place in the over-all series and not the order of publication.

All titles are subject to change.